DEROS
FOR THE UNDEFEATED

A Novel

Dr. Buzz Harrison, M.D.

Library of Congress Cataloging-in-Publication Data

DEROS for the Undefeated

© 2015 by Dr. Buzz Harrison, M.D. All rights reserved.

ISBN: 978-0-9908602-0-4

Library of Congress Control Number: 2015907519

Editing by Michelle C. Booth
Production Management by Sandy Dolan
Front Cover Photo by Lissandra Melo
Back Cover Photo by Matthew Carroll
Interior Design and Formatting by Penelope Love

To contact the publisher, email: CherBeePress@gmail.com

DEDICATION

From a son, grateful under God, a dedication to a father, a father-in-law, a brother, a brother-in-law, an aunt, cousins, and many other fighters for liberty and justice who proudly, in the American military, served their country with distinction. *And **without** defeat!*

ACKNOWLEDGMENTS

In almost every creative endeavor, specific and special people contribute in producing the finished product by their encouragements, insights, and suggestions. In the case of writing a novel, exceptional readers, reviewers, and refiners share their personal time to engage the characters along real and imagined journeys.

With loving appreciation, I would like to express heartfelt gratitude to my wife, son, sister, brother-in-law, and brother: Cherry, Mark, Barbara, Dan, and Dave. Without their help over a prolonged period of laboring with this project, I would have stopped plodding through plots and penning in pencil long ago.

And finally, in regards to those who assisted in the proofreading, editing, and publishing of this manuscript, your service and expertise were to me, invaluable.

INTRODUCTION

It startled every fiber which innervates the senses of feeling and hearing in the human body—a sonic shock wave. The earth quaked like at Jericho when the walls came tumbling down. The air was electrified like lightning striking nearby with its instantaneous colossal thunderclap. This outburst was similar to an excessively loud response one might hear from boisterous fans attending a fall football game some sunny Saturday afternoon. Yes, it was fall; yes, it was sunny; and yes, it was a Saturday—yet no stadium filled with football fanatics—***Vietnam was not a game. It was a war!***

The roar of the crowd had emanated from an adjacent airplane hangar. The noisy eruption had ended almost as abruptly as it had begun, as if stifled by a maestro's choral cutoff: three seconds of *"yea!"* sounding like a sustained, thick-accented *"yea-es"* (yes) sharply cancelled by the envisioned baton stroke slicing down through the air. The result was stark dead silence. Landing at Bien Hoa Airbase, Captain Adam Barnes, U.S. Army Medical Corps, had just touched down on the red clay soil of Vietnam—a dust, which when airborne, soon would permeate his shirts, shorts, shoes… and soul—forever it would seem.

Dr. Barnes made his way with a number of other "newbies" toward an open air pavilion. His comrade soldiers were puzzled by the outcry too. Nonchalantly, in their own way, each was trying not to show their curiosity or disquietude. They walked tall, or they strode cool, or they took a slow, subtle but deep breath. Earlier, from a vantage point on the forward stairway platform affixed to the aircraft exit, each soldier's welcome reception was comprised of three distinct components: blinding light from rainbow-esque sunbursts reflecting off polished aluminum Quonsets, oppressive heat visible as a rising misty layer of mirage, and thirdly that ecstatic exclamation of energy embodied in one solitary shout.

The cheer was not a greeting, but a farewell to arms for about 100 Vietnam veterans, who had just completed their "365 and a wake-up." The short-timers' calendars had been completely colored in for these deeply tanned, dust-covered, battle weary combatants. Touchdown would come with *liftoff*. For them, *it was DEROS day.*

After the new arrivals had disembarked, the return flight's boarding-call boomed over the loudspeaker. Those waiting would not need a second or final call. Obviously, these warriors were ready to head home. The Golden Gate of San Francisco beckoned, and Travis Air Force Base would be an acceptable destination for getting back to the world. *It was DEROS day.*

Oddly enough, the shout, that first tumultuous tremor of intonation, was just a prelude to a second spontaneity of manly exuberance. The heavens above will be treated to another resounding cheer from this all-male chorus. Crackling over the intercom the pilot will interrupt to say, "This is the Captain speaking. Our plane has just departed the airspace of the Republic of Vietnam."

The cabin shell will shake as if traversing in turbulent thunderclouds. The unison shout will be quickly extinguished as before, but this time the muffling will be accompanied by muted murmurings, nervous laughter, and audibly sustained sighs of relief. Soldier smiles and gleeful grins will be acknowledged by all the airline stewardesses, since such a sonic boom they will have experienced multiple times before. These air angels all too well understood what it meant for these men to be going home. *It was DEROS day!* But what about *those* men for whom it was not?

DEROS
FOR THE UNDEFEATED

CHAPTER 1

FROM SAWBONES
TO SURGEONS

In another time a century past, in a new nation beyond the sea of peace, *a south* was engaged in *a war* with a *north*. The battlefields were the valleys of Caroline County, Virginia. One day after the sun had spectacularly lowered her head for sleep and a full moon yawned into arising, the tragedy of *war* came home.

Some soldiers bivouacked down for rest in their Confederate tents; some generals stayed awake pacing and planning the next day's field strategy; and a comrade in arms contingent of North Carolina militiamen stationed themselves on the camp perimeter as a firing line to guard the forward fringe.

Early in the watch a muffled whinny was heard in the distance blending confusingly with the whine of the blowing wind. Afterwards the ominous sounds of snapping twigs and dry leaves crunching under hooves alerted the line in the direction of the grove of trees facing them from the north. Nothing was yet visible except for the towering spires of pine branches, their tree trunks staggered in rows arrayed like a picket of posts. Finally, outlined from the rear by rays of moonlight, steeds with shadowy figures bestraddling their backs appeared in the open gaps as these horses coursed behind the trees. The animals moved with graceful strides at an easy walking gait which quickened to a loping trot as they emerged from their arbored cover.

From the campsite edge of the clearing came a cry, "Yankee cavalry!" followed by an earsplitting yell from one of the Johnny Rebs. Flint sparks from Fayetteville rifles flashed to frame the shouters and the shooters in their rifle-raised stances. The skirmish was one sided and brief before a second, more authoritative command echoed, "Cease firing! Cease firing! It's our boys!"

Amidst the chaotic flurry of equestrian activity: stomping in place, rearing up, snorting and neighing, the shadow riders dismounted and rushed to a fallen horseman who had been knocked out of the saddle by the impact of a musket rifle round. The minnie ball had struck his left arm midway between the shoulder and the elbow joint. The bullet slashed through uniform and flesh splintering the man's humerus. Fragments of bone exploded piercing the sinew and skin in all directions. The wound was severe; the bleeding, profuse. General Thomas "Stonewall" Jackson had been accidentally shot by his own troops, men he had led in a resoundingly victorious way that very afternoon against the Union soldiers near Chancellorsville. The general and his aides had been out on reconnaissance: scouting, surveying, probing and planning for a possible follow-up night strike on the Northern forces.

"Get the general to the doc!" cried out the sergeant of the sentry duty detachment. Gingerly Jackson was transported to the surgical tent where Doctor Newton Barnes had just completed another amputation and was washing up at a basin in the corner when the flap of entryway canvas was raised. Reverentially the wounded man was processioned in on a stretcher and painstakingly transferred onto the block wooden table in the center of the room, one companion cradling in sling-like support the General's limp left extremity.

No military formality by the field surgeon here. "Not you, Tom?" With a bloodstained, white apron suspended from his neck, he leaned his upper torso over the edge of the table and pulled a hanging lantern for a closer look.

The patient slumped his head toward the doctor and replied in a weak whisper, "Newt."

The history of these two men went way back. They knew each other from their childhood days in Lewis County, Virginia (now West Virginia). As boys, they used to hunt in the same hills and fish in the same streams around Jackson's Mill, home place acreage for the Jackson clan.

Tommy Jackson lost both his parents at the age of seven, and as an orphan was whisked over the mountain to the mill community populated by many of his kin. He was reared by a parental bachelor uncle named Cummins Jackson and a step grandmother. After spending about a dozen years working with his uncle in Jackson's Mill, at the age of eighteen he received an appointment to the West Point Academy. Tom Jackson chose the study of military science. On the other hand, in nearby Weston, Newton Barnes opted to further his education in the science of medicine.

In adulthood, the lives of these two old friends had not crossed until this war between the states. Doctor Barnes, now in his early forties, had been, in essence, conscripted into the Confederate Army after the Federal Armory at Harpers Ferry was captured and Colonel Thomas J. Jackson was placed in command. The unique understanding between the military superior and his doctor friend allowed Barnes to remain (assigned) in the region of the Shenandoah Valley functioning as a kind of neutral itinerant healer for both sides. Jackson, as a Christian, respected Barnes' conscientious stance to serve all the sick and injured— no matter on what side they fought, North or South. He was painfully aware of how this civil war was pitting family against family, neighbor against neighbor, even brother against brother. That fateful night near Chancellorsville happened to be the only time the two friends from Lewis County had seen each other in about a year. The reunion tragically would be short.

When Stonewall Jackson's head slumped, it was because he had lapsed into unconsciousness, succumbing to the effects of massive blood loss and shock. Time was of the essence. Hemorrhage from the multiple lacerations of the arteries below the armpit was life threatening. Simple compression could not stop the flow. The arm wound was so gaping and the bone so shattered that amputation was the only option if the bleeding was to be brought under control.

Finding and removing the half-inch sized cone of lead culprit which had caused such extreme mangling of the extremity was not the major problem. Again, the gushing blood was. In fact, the spherical projectile, all of its destructive energy now spent, fell onto the table with a plumbic plunk as the axillary tourniquet and restraining straps were being applied. Shredded tissue was debrided, the humerus bone was severed high with a hand saw, and a primary closure was performed. (A secondary closure and stump would have to come days later.) The bleeding from the brachial artery slowed to an ooze as the tied off vessel contracted and clots began to form.

The surgery was gruesome and quick. However, with the discovery of effective antibiotics like sulfa and penicillin being delayed into the next century of war, within the second week the patient died of a dreaded post-operative complication: pneumonia. On a Sunday morning, the dawn of a fresh first day, during one of those terminal intervals of lucid reflection, Stonewall Jackson uttered his final words within hearing range of his boyhood playmate who was holding prayerful vigilance at his bedside. "Let us cross over the river and rest under the shade of the old Mill trees."

With that, he gazed intently into the heavens. His lids sank slowly down covering his pale blue eyes and then he calmly journeyed home—undaunted and undefeated even in death.

————————

The Civil rivalry between the Northern States and the Southern States was not a war game. It was a state of total war! Over a half of a million casualties occurred in the conflict about establishing rights for all free people. Historically, freedom has never been free—taken for granted, yes, but never free.

————————

Though often hunted and pursued by Confederate and Union sympathizers alike, Doctor Newton Barnes survived in his surreptitious comings and goings across the Virginia valley battlefields until the war's end at Appomattox Court House and the surrender of General Robert E. Lee in April of 1865. However, as threats against his family became more serious during the war, Barnes chose to send his wife and children to hide and live with relatives in Ohio. These menacing repercussions were generated by the doctor's humanitarian neutrality in treating the injured and the ill of *both* the North *and* the South.

Upon returning to Lewis County, the country physician resumed his medical practice in Weston, a small railway town, now a part of the newly declared state of West Virginia. He died before the turn of the century, leaving behind a wife, two daughters, and a son born in 1861 as a war baby. Because of the friendship between the physician father and the famous military fighter, the infant boy was christened with the name "Thomas" in honor of Thomas Stonewall Jackson. Being only two years old at the time, young Thomas never had the privilege of meeting his namesake because of the general's unfortunate and untimely death.

Thomas Newton Barnes followed in the footsteps of his father taking the path of medicine and practicing that art well into the twentieth century. The lineage of military doctors did remain intact.

In 1898, with the Spanish American War, Tom Barnes, feeling the need to serve his country, volunteered for the Rough Riders, the American Cavalry regiment organized by Teddy Roosevelt. He was drawn to this branch of military service because of his love of horses, even though his family only owned one, a plow horse puller of the field wagon. Nevertheless, riding bareback on this old plug above the banks of the West Fork River out to "The Mill," spending the day refreshing in the cool pond, and then retracing the path south before the night's darkness could overtake him was a favorite summer pastime in his youth. Lazily he would lean slouched back to back across the horse's rump. The farm animal knew the way home, or at least to the Barnes' barn—and that was near enough.

Prior to joining the Rough Riders and performing the duties of a field medic in Puerto Rico, Barnes had gained permission to court a pretty and petite West Virginia girl from the Proudfoot family of Grafton. The two of them were an odd looking couple. He, six foot four; and she, barely four foot six. The sparks of an infatuation courtship were fanned to flames of unconditional love when Tom returned from the hills of San Juan to the hills of West Virginia. The two, he in his thirties and she in her twenties, married within a year of his muster out of the armed forces.

Over the next ten years, six girls were the result of the union of Tom Barnes and Mattie Proudfoot—no sons! However, in the course of time, a late life surprise, a boy was born. The year was 1911. Doctor Barnes had just turned fifty years of age.

With the woods and waters of the West Fork River Basin providing a vast playground for gatherings of generations—past, present, and for the future—it was only fitting that one day Tom's son Franklin Theodore Barnes by name, would meet and later marry a daughter descendant of Stonewall Jackson. And so it happened. At a camp called Jackson's Mill.

The granddaughter's name was Jessie Joan Jackson (the "Joan," stressed by her father, to be pronounced "Jo Ann"). In an evening gown dancing or in bib overalls milking a cow, she was an eye catcher. On the other hand, the little lady played the roll of tomboy for her dad in a family of females.

Friends and close acquaintances called her "Jo." However, she endured a lot of teasing because of the name similarity of "Jo Jackson" with the infamous "Shoeless Joe Jackson," who was reported to have conspired in the fixing of the 1919 Baseball World

Series, the Chicago "Black Sox" scandal. She was an outstanding athlete and never would have thrown a game for any reason. She was too competitive, too principled, and too proud.

Frank Barnes exuded athletic sweat and exhibited sport's prowess too, but it would not be recreational games on a field of play that would bring the two individuals together. Strangely enough, the venue for their first encounter was a simple field of hay. The non-sport extracurricular activity they both enjoyed was 4-H.

In the early years the tenets of 4-H (Head, Heart, Hands and Health) needed to be spotlighted in a memorable fashion for public relations purposes. Club administrators wanted to feature two teens, one boy and one girl, who as active participants in 4-H could exemplify by means of a symbolic logo the qualities of good health and moral character for the members of the clubs and the attenders of the camps. The Mountain State search was conducted one summer at Jackson's Mill. Coincidentally, candidate choices were eliminated down to the selection of Frank and Jo. At this point in their lives they were nothing more than friends, but providence had paired them for the future.

The highlight of the camp publicity campaign was an iconographic poster depicting the two youths superimposed and bracketing an upright millstone—a real granite wheel about five feet tall and one foot thick. As silhouetted campers, Frank and Jo stand with their arms outstretched and reaching toward the heavens, their heads uplifted as if acknowledging the Creator of all that is portrayed around them in the picturesque background. The hilltop view of the valley below details a panorama of the Jackson's Mill Camp: the white painted buildings and the white-washed bridges, the wood cabins and the campfire circles, the playing fields, swimming pool, and the winding river which encircled it all, 4-H personified in picture-postcard form.

What an honor for these two teens to represent all the youthful members of 4-H programs across the state and beyond—their hopes, their dreams. More significantly, they would not just know them but actively embrace these qualities by which they would grow as persons.

With a touch of predestinate irony, these two youthful icons would in seven years leave their parents and become husband and wife. As the Good Book defines marriage, "the two shall become one." Such was the case for a Barnes and a Jackson.

In their lifetime they had experienced *the war to end all wars* and endured it—*the Great Depression to end all depressions*—and endured it. And now, having migrated south to the Kanawha Valley and the city of South Charleston, they could settle down to the process of producing a family in peace to pass on the values learned from their forefathers to a new generation. Unfortunately a progeny at peace can be propagandized into a progeny for war. Standing in stark contrast would be two West Virginia youths with both arms upraised in reverence to God versus two European youths with a single arm uplifted in salute of allegiance to their fuehrer as a god. Lurking and looming on the horizon, masquerading overseas as *games*—the 1936 Berlin Olympics—old rivals were rearming for *war*.

CHAPTER 2

PRESEASON FOR WAR GAMES

M any years would pass before Frank and Jo Barnes would venture from the *North* back into the *South*. Once again it would be a time of war. Surviving the Depression as young marrieds, they started over with nothing and were building it into something. Then Pearl Harbor was bombed. Jo was pregnant with their second child. The baby boy about to be delivered would be the only Barnes ever to be born away from the hills of West Virginia.

A tracing of 100 years of "war-doc" history in the lineage of Barnes-Jackson would reveal that standing as the last in this century-long line is an Adam. In the Bible, after the five most important words of preamble, "In the beginning God created," the reader is introduced to the first man, Adam, upon whom the first surgery is performed (a thoracectomy, i.e., rib removal). In the future, the war-baby Barnes would be destined to become another general medical officer in the army; but a surgeon he never planned to be.

Adam Barnes was a physician fresh from a pediatric internship at Children's Hospital in Akron, Ohio. He had been enrolled in the medical call-up issued by President Lyndon B. Johnson in in 1968—one of two doctors drafted from West Virginia. The instant his plane touched down on Vietnam soil, the DEROS time clock was triggered, ticking inexorably toward "short" days and those two heaven-shattering shouts. Almost from infancy, due to the wartime circumstances of his birth in 1942, Adam Barnes had been nurtured to love God and country—to be a good citizen—to support and defend the Constitution of United States of America. So a two-year commitment of military discipline seemed a natural response to these ingrained sentiments—although the majority of early baby boomers had a differing viewpoint, especially with regard to that serving thing called the draft. The generation ahead of Barnes had gone willingly; the generation after him would go reluctantly. For the former, there was no such thing as DEROS, only V-E Day and V-J Day—victory. For the latter group, just DEROS (Date Estimated Return from OverSeas).

Barnes was proud of the patriotism of his parents and the mountaineer stock from which they had come. Nevertheless, enduring the separation, he bitterly missed being around his father in the formative years of his childhood. His dad had been a major in the U.S. Army during World War II (later seeing action on the beaches of Normandy and at the Battle of the Bulge in Europe).

During the stateside training of his father, Adam's mother, a steely strong woman tempered with godly faith, had traveled and travailed with her husband across the South, from army base to army base. She was caring for a two-year-old daughter while carrying Adam in the third trimester of her pregnancy. She had chosen to do so in order to be supportive totally of her soulmate before he was shipped overseas, the actual embarkation date falling just weeks after Adam's birth.

After the World War II era, neither parent pushed the premise of an owed military commitment. *They knew war.* However, it seemed mostly an unspoken cultural precept among those who dearly loved their freedom (West Virginia State motto: "Mountaineers are always free"). For young Adam, service to one's country had become an inner calling. He naively assumed that every American shared the same feeling. Liberty was a gift handed down over the ages with sacrifices made from Valley Forge to Vietnam. Sacrifices offered freely in opposition to terroristic aggression and brutal oppression against the weak and innocent. Every human creature of God, from Adam to this generation of people should taste freedom fully in their lifetime he believed. Was it not an inalienable right from above—a right in his day which unfortunately needed to be championed?

For Barnes, being the second child in the family fostered two traits which evolved early in the home of four children (one girl and three boys). These traits were sibling rivalry and competitive spirit—a strong competitive spirit. Besting a rival opponent, even if it was only your older sister, seemed paramount. (At the end of one of these contestings, this beloved sister had a rejoinder that always stopped Adam in his tracks, especially the first time that she used it. "Little Brother, you sure have long arms!" "What do you mean, Sis?" he asked, thinking her words may embody a subtle compliment to the victor. However, her clever comeback was sharper than any two-edged sword. "You have long arms, the better to pat yourself on the back!" Pierced to the heart…again.)

In time these driving energies within Barnes manifested themselves primarily in academics and athletics. The fact that both parents had succeeded as students and sportsmen themselves only added to his desire to emulate their work ethic. The learned goal was to win by exerting great effort and by playing fair and square. When the objective of victory was achieved, it was to be couched in genuine humility as a good show of sportsmanship. Cockiness was never tolerated in the home or on the field. Adam's parents and sister saw to that.

The sport of his mother, basketball, turned out to be Adam Barnes' most successful athletic endeavor, even though football, the sport of his father, was the more natural one for him. Yet on the one hand, Adam never matched his father's feat of four running touchdowns in one game on the football field; on the other, neither could he duplicate the scoring accomplishments of his mother on the hardwoods. She averaged for her high school *career* a whopping 28 points per game. Adam, in contrast, scored his career high of 28 in only one game—though a most memorable game at that. (The mother scored her points when a player received only one point if the shot was one handed from over the head, while the son played prior to the advent of the three-point goal.)

In basketball, Adam was a center by height but agile enough to play point guard. In football he was a good quarterback with one deficiency. He lacked bulk. No matter how much he ate (and he was a bottomless pit, eating six peanut butter and jelly sandwiches a day), his metabolism burned it off. He would describe himself with the adjectives, "lean" and "slender;" but at six foot three and 160 pounds, he was excessively thin and "skinny" no matter what he saw or what he said. To the public, however, his elongated, gaunt face and his brown, receding hair wave might suggest the implausibility of his being an athlete. But from an early age, growing up beside the local stadium wall, an all-around athlete he was.

From adolescence to adulthood, keen team rivalries in both basketball and football continued to provide challenges at every level of sport. Interscholastically and intercollegiately, Adam was rarely accustomed to losing in games. His teams amassed an uncanny record of victories with championships at each and every tier of competition. Yet his rivalry record of success was what stood out. Barnes never lost an *arch-rivalry* game throughout his athletic career; never in elementary school, junior high, senior high, or college! *Never!*

In the sports world there were these legendary rivalries: those annual competitions of teams that had a long tradition, heated historical match ups between fierce competitors like the New York Yankees and Brooklyn Dodgers in baseball, Michigan and Ohio State in football, and Duke University and North Carolina in basketball; epic battles for bragging rights—opponents who literally did not like each other, grudge-laded contests. In the privacy of his conscious self, Adam Barnes was motivated by the famous public address announcer's designation for a winning boxer, "Undefeated—and still champion." Such for him was the ultimate goal in a rivalry, whether in sports or in life.

Winning when one was not supposed to win held an even greater attraction for Barnes. He loved the challenge of being the underdog. Often in pick-up games he would handicap himself with lesser talented players who were not accustomed to winning. He would do this in order to share the thrill of victory. In most cases, against the odds, he would win the game over the more superior competitors. Coming from behind and pulling out a victory at the last second was a thrilling and sought-after predicament. Three times in competition, a successful final shot at the buzzer spelled the eventual outcome for his basketball team.

However, it was because of his football talent that a door was opened to play college basketball. James Carlton, a football recruiter from Duke in Durham, North Carolina, had been made aware of Barnes' prowess as a two-sport star. Upon his recommendation the basketball staff offered a scholarship. (In the back of his mind, Carlton believed that if Barnes did not make it in basketball, he would have a quarterback for his football team. Each spring in the weight room, the coach would challenge the basketball player with a sarcastic inquiry. "When are you going to give up this sissy sport and come play football?")

In Barnes' mind it was a privilege to play a game and receive an education at the same time. With parental encouragement, Adam sent his head coach a thank-you card for that privilege after each completed season. In addition, he felt extremely fortunate to play in the early sixties on teams which arguably were the best scholar-athlete teams on the court and in the classroom for the modern history of NCAA basketball. (To be eligible to play Division I sports and receive a scholarship in the Atlantic Coast Conference during the 50s and 60s, a high school graduate had to attain a 1000 to 1600 SAT score on the College Board exam. Therefore, "academic athlete" would seem to be a more appropriate moniker than "student athlete" in that era. Barnes weighed in somewhere between 1000 and 1100, bouncing off the bottom of his recruiting class, while his six foot ten inch roommate aced the SATs having an IQ of more than 140.) In the case of the ACC, an athletic scholarship had to be earned with the balance of college preparation academically in high school. Once enrolled in collegiate classes, scholastic grade averages had to be maintained in order to be permitted to play.)

At Duke in 1964, more combination Academic All-Americans

existed at the time on the basketball team than National Collegiate All-Americans (three to one). Six earned doctorates were eventually bestowed upon the top seven players on that team, from undergraduate degrees in pre-med, pre-law, physics, accounting, education and engineering. Of these magnificent seven, Adam considered himself the "curve booster" at the bottom for the high standard of team academic achievement.

Athletically, among his Blue Devil colleagues Adam Barnes would grade himself landing somewhere on the middle of the curve. He happened to be a good athlete who had those occasional, memorable moments of greatness in his sports career. He played with and against others who were more gifted than he, but none could beat him in individual effort. He believed that total effortful labor, exhausting every ounce of energy, could make a winner out of any person, athlete or soldier, even when the scoreboard indicated a defeat in the record book.

Be that as it may, ***Vietnam was not a game. It was a war!*** Yet Barnes' only knowledge of Vietnam and the war was primarily related to a game—a game he played in the summer of '64—a game peculiarly named "Cong." Where did he learn to play this game? Of all places, it was at a camp for kids called Jackson's Mill.

CHAPTER 3

NIGHT LIGHT

Adam Barnes found great enjoyment working with animals and playing with children. Both held a tender place in his heart. If he had not been accepted into Duke Medical School with the goal of becoming a pediatrician, he probably would have gone to veterinary school. Success in either field would have been most gratifying to Barnes. As to which was the more favored, babies or puppies, it made minimal difference. Both were extra special creations of God to be loved and protected.

This dual devotion to the care of children and animals led Barnes on summer excursions to the West Fork River as a camp counselor at Jackson's Mill. While other Duke medical students spent their seasonal breaks assisting in research labs or hospital clinics, Barnes returned to his roots teaching sport skills and playing all manner of games with pre-pubescent kids. At this particular camp he could also function as an amateur veterinarian serving as midwife in the delivery of newborn colts at the riding stables or shoveling manure out of the stalls.

Another of his assigned responsibilities at this co-ed camp was to take groups of eight-to ten-year-old boys on covered wagon overnights—cooking on campfires and sleeping under the stars on the hard ground. The wagon was pulled by a team of white work horses. One was old, moon-blinded and experienced; the other was a young, rambunctious rambler. The old steadied the young; the young guided the blind. Harnessed together they were a team—fun to drive and fun to care for.

The young campers delighted in the wagon ride along the scenic backwoods trail, pothole bumps and small stream splashes notwithstanding. Regardless of what ruckus was happening in the wagon, the horses continued their steady plod unperturbed. It was a grand, if not uproarious, nature outing for city boys.

However, these wilderness treks almost were discontinued after the first wagon expedition of the camping season. On that initial adventure when all the campers had tucked themselves into their zip around bed rolls and when the occasional hollow sounding hoot of a horned owl no longer startled their suspended consciousness, Adam Barnes enjoyed the long awaited lull beside the wood campfire with its sparking snaps and glowing embers. As a self-imposed night owl, the wagon team counselor never retired to sleep until the fire was completely extinguished. The time was approaching eleven o'clock.

Late evening during that reverent hush over the hills which often enhanced the star shrouded valley into a refuge, a natural outer sanctum of peace and quiet, the two wagon work horses suddenly stirred as they grazed nearby. Shortly thereafter, both simultaneously shifted their positions in the cove. These two steeds were not known to be skittish animals. Laid-back swaybacks was a more fitting description. Clearly, something was disturbing their usual calm. The snorting whinnies of alarm, short lived, became diminished at the equines' newly rotated location on the anchor stake's circumferential boundary.

Barnes rose from the log on which he was sitting, shielding his vision from the smoldering fire to peer out toward the neighing horses in the meadow. Out of the corner of his eye he glimpsed a slithering shadow sinuously coursing from the grass field stobs and gliding over the ground surface of the cleared campfire circle. Adam became rigid beyond motionless. He was terrified into the first stage of petrification. The four-foot-long snake frightened a faint rattling sound as it paused, then steered along the edge stealthily toward a row of sleeping bags with bedded down boys, sound asleep and oblivious to the side winding, venomous visitor.

Barnes, frozen in form, visually scanned for a tool, a weapon. Even if he was able to spy something near enough to grasp, he physically felt totally incapacitated to react. His vocal cords seemed paralyzed with the rest of his body's musculature. On a cold mountain's night the inviting apertures of the quilt-lined bags were signaling a temporary respite of darkness and warmth to the interloping reptile, now less than two yards away from the unsuspecting slumberers. "Lord, help!"

Out of the smoke murky sky came a swoop—the feathery *whoosh* of pierced air being the only audible sound that Adam detected. The rattlesnake vanished. One instant, the unseen threat was there—unseen to all but one in the owl-light of night—the next, it was gone, swiftly, tightly clasped in the strong talons of a nocturnal bird of prey. Adam collapsed limply to his knees. Recovering tonicity, he mentally decided that the event would go unreported except to the camp director—in the morning. Until then, the campsite would remain under the watchful gaze of the wagon master until dawn lifted lazily over the valley's natural trellis line of trees along the eastern horizon.

From the uninitiated perspective of the kids, the highlight of their dreaming that night was not the averted encounter with a serpentine intruder. More than likely, their dreams reflected upon the after dinner activities associated with the much anticipated group game known as Cong. (Vietnam terminology was subliminally intrusive to the mind without conjuring up images of that ongoing real war.) Cong was devised by the camp staff as a cross between "capture the flag" and a night version of "kick the can." The valley in which the event took place was Norman Rockwell serene with a tree lined lake to the north and an open meadow to the south.

Two groups of campers participated in this activity: <u>Mule Train</u>, the pack-mule hiking team, and <u>Wagon One</u>, the covered-wagon team. The mule bunch would establish a campsite above the lake on a promontory wooded with pine trees. Wagon One, because of their horses, would set up below the pond's earthen dam in the grassy expanse beyond the spillway.

Each base camp would have a team flag, usually a towel or T-shirt, attached to a stick anchored upright in the ground. In the blackness, without benefit of flashlights (except in emergencies or in cases of panic attacks by eight-year-olds afraid of the dark), the teams would move across a no-man's-land field on their way to capturing the rival team's flag. The challenge was to bring the flag back without being captured themselves. The game would end when the opponent's flag was raised in the victorious camp.

The capture of prisoners was an important part of the strategy, thus a means of reducing the number of available flag retrievers. To capture a prisoner, a player needed to tag the individual with a "grenade." These make-shift grenades were really just the oblong shaped pods from the Saucer Magnolia trees which were abundant along the trail to the lake.

These pods by rule had to be thrown underhanded, and the toss had to make contact below the waist in order for the contestant to be considered tagged as a prisoner-of-war. Sworn to an honor system these captured players then must walk directly to their opponents prison plot with hands held over their heads. Once in jail, they could be freed by being touched by a free-moving member of their team.

Recounting the goal of the game, in order to win, one team had to capture the opposing team's flag and return with it to their home base of operations safely without being captured and imprisoned.

Usually in the first thirty minutes of the game, the tactics were deliberately left to the ingenuity, or lack thereof, of the young campers themselves. The staff members and junior counselors would sit on the sidelines overseeing for the purpose of safety. The thrill for a child is the scariness of the dark. Needless to say, these miniature men rarely ventured far from the light of their respective campfires. If they did decide to be bold and move out into the blackness of the field of play, within two minutes of advancement, a flurry of flashlight commotion could be detected. Multiple retreating balls of light could be seen bouncing their way back to base in opposite directions like scattering lightning bugs.

The activity would pick up considerably at the start of the second half hour when all the staff counselors could strategically assist their minions by joining in the frantic free-for-all. The hard part of each competition was not the capture, but rather the maneuvering safely back through the dark to one's home base with the opponent's flag.

Adam Barnes had cleverly designed a strategy for retrieving his team's lost flag while capturing the rival flag in the process. From his oversight position on the adjacent hillside, he would observe the campers' flashing light movements about the valley—and intently listen. He was listening for the inevitable four word cry from Wagon One's eight-year-old goalie. "They've got our flag!" Before the final echo of the word flag reverberated across the valley, Barnes would already have sprung into action.

From his vantage point of the high ground Barnes would immediately traverse the meadow with alarming speed for moving without a flashlight in the darkness. He would scale the spillway, outrunning the slowly retreating opponents. He then would outmaneuver them through the cove of trees without making a sound, in like manner as a tiny bird gliding through the full foliage of a tree without rustling a leaf. His plan was to stay ahead of their logical path until the perfect moment of a surprise intersecting ambush of the flag thief. One accurate pod toss and the covered-wagon pole and pennant would be recaptured.

Shortly thereafter, all the imprisoned wagon members would be freed with a hand tag from the darting and dashing spirit sprinter. Snatching the enemy flag and encouraging his members to begin their long free walk back to base camp, Barnes disappeared phantom-like into the night with uncanny agility. His return route was more circuitous to avoid the enemy rush to trap him. His sudden appearance with both flags at the home base campfire almost always startled his youthful charges followed by a spontaneous shout of triumph resonating as a decrescendo of echoes across the valley.

The Wagon One gang never lost a game of Cong that whole summer of weekly contests. The reason they never lost was a secret known only to Adam Barnes. He had a distinct advantage over everyone else that guaranteed victory, especially in the dark.

————————

From about the age of these young campers Adam was noted to have a highly competitive spirit instilled within him, in some sense even an exaggerated streak. Curious about its presence at such a young age, his first grade teacher discussed its intensity with Barnes' parents at PTA evaluations. From where did such a dynamic drive come—this drive to be the very best in the classroom and on the playground?

The fine line between being defeated and losing was not *fine* to Barnes. One could be defeated by a better team made up of more skilled athletes or of physically more mature players. On the other hand, losing seemed to imply a lack of effort, a failure to put forth one's best effort. Theoretically, Barnes believed that an individual could be a winner in effort in every contest.

Based on this personal prescript for life, Barnes progressed to contribute to a variety of triumphant teams. (The compulsion to win a *rivalry* game, especially against a better team, would often supersede winning a conference title. Just be sure the rivalry result was a "W" not an "L." That was his philosophy.)

For Barnes, his undefeated streak against rivals started at his earliest stages of team competitions. Later, football trophies were retired. Championships at every level were won: county, state, and national conferences. Individual honors would come, but family oversight always encouraged, if not enforced, a spirit of humility. The successes of the team would produce honor, respect, and accolades to the individual. No greater ingredient for victory existed than merging the total efforts of every individual member on a team. One for all and all for one. E Pluribus Unum. Out of the many, one!

All this sport philosophy, though well and good, was not the main reason why Barnes was undefeated in the camp game of Cong. His secret? He could literally see in the dark. Seeing what no one else can see—objects in the pitch-black of night hidden from the naked eye—was an advantage in a game like Cong, especially if the trait was unknown to any of the participants. Barnes was able to use this secret aptitude to exploit the cover of darkness. What does an owl see in its night-enshrouded surroundings? Miraculously Adam Barnes had experienced the answer since he was a teenager. How he acquired the gift of "night sight" would have intrigued even the most skeptical.

Like most mountain state houses in South Charleston, West Virginia, his childhood home was bedrock-fastened on the side of a hilltop ridge. His back porch overlooked a small, sheltered valley called Joplin Hollow. Such a rustic terrain provided the perfect playground of paths, caves, and shallow streams. Huge gray granite boulders deposited by some prehistoric glacier dotted the hillside. Along with an elevated perimeter of rocky cliffs, carved out by eons of fast moving water, these natural formations fashioned a young boy's paradise for play.

Barnes and his companions would often wage games of cowboys and Indians, pirates and buccaneers, soldiers and warriors in these woods. Like Robin Hood's merry men in Sherwood Forest, they practiced the ancient arts of warfare—sword fighting with sticks, staff jousting with tree limbs, and arrow shooting with homemade bows.

Exploring the surface crags and crevices of the cliffs was always fun. However, Barnes was deathly afraid of crawling underground into dark tunnels, damp caverns, and unknown mines—all of which were prevalent in the area. Exhibiting a claustrophobic side was unusual for the usually bold and adventurous Barnes.

Why the fear? It may have arisen subconsciously from his exposure to the Tom Sawyer cave saga with Injun Joe in Mark Twain's novel or from an inherent fear of encountering snakes in dark spaces. A bedtime story his mother often read to him called *Peter Rabbit* included a frightful account of Peter coming face-to-face with a terrifying snake, vividly animated in the margins of the page. The reptile depicted was threateningly large and coiled to strike; angry eyes aglow, fangs unfurled and glistening in the summer sun as venom dripped from the two pointed tips. Yet a more impressionable family story may have fed Adam's fear of reptilian slitherers inhabiting the subterranean world.

———————————

Barnes as a child believer, had postponed his rite of passage into the Christian faith because of a recounted incident which happened at his mother's own baptism in the West Fork River. She was at the tender age of eight. The worship site embodied one of those riverscape vistas "beside the still waters." The spot was located just above Jackson's Mill where the stream flowed so imperceptibly slow that the surface appeared to be one continuous mirror. The spillway and dam barriers created a natural reflecting pool for the horseshoe horizon of hills that cradled the mill camp. Over the years that picturesque point of land had become the perfect place for an outdoor baptismal service at the river.

On that day in 1917, the sun dazzled brightly off the bleached white robes of the candidates, young and old. Facing the mill from the sloping east bank, community and congregant observers along with family and friends were seated or standing. Traditionally, baptisms were to be performed in moving water as in the days of Jesus, the Jordan River, and John the Baptist. In addition, the channel depth of the river had to accommodate the total immersion of the believer's body. The Greek term, "baptism," translated in the Bible described a wholly sunken ship.

The early Christians called baptism a "sacramentum"—a Latin word for the Roman soldier's oath of absolute allegiance and obedience to his commanding general. To the religious neophyte, baptism symbolized the absolute allegiance and obedience to their general, the Lord Jesus Christ. The submerging motion identified the convert with the death and burial of Christ (a dying to the old life); the upraising from beneath the water represented the rebirth of a transformed person. Exiting the river was the final step of initiation to a new life: death to the old way, resurrection to a new commitment to God, to a new personal walk with Christ, to a totally new way of living.

As the assembled choir members sang from the shore the words of Robert Lowry's hymn, "…Yes, we'll gather at the river, The beautiful, the beautiful river…" individual candidates waded into the water beyond the adjacent sandbar beach. Waiting mid-channel would be the administering pastor and an assisting church deacon whose sole purpose was to stabilize the minister's stance on the uneven and irregular river bottom.

On the day of Barnes' mother's baptism the current was surprisingly swift and caused the minister to be coaxed progressively downstream with each successive immersion. Using his open palms, the deacon kept a steady pressure to the back of the pastor quietly encouraging him to stride and slide upstream away from a large, flat-surface boulder positioned in the middle of the stream. Then abruptly, the deacon became quite emphatic with his physical urgings to the extent of frustrating the pastor. In exasperation, the minister, who was about to lower Adam's mother into the ritual waters, wheeled his head toward the downstream deacon and demanded to know why the man kept pushing him so forcefully. The deacon's response was irreverently blunt. "Peas and rice, Reverend, didn't you see that huge, blankety-blank, water moccasin sunning on that boulder in the middle of the river?"

Needless to say, the pastoral procession including Adam's mother moved without further ado upstream as the music echoed "Gather the saints at the river that flows by the throne of God."

When Adam first heard this account of his mother's experience from his uncle, the minister who performed the baptism, the image of cottonmouth vipers in the river became an impediment for his submitting to the sacrament as a child until indoor church baptistries became the order of the day. Yet for Adam baptism never relieved his anxiety of encountering snake eyes in the close confines of the underground.

Whatever the traumatizing cause, such a fear was deeply conditioned into the mind of the young Barnes to the extreme point that he would never venture down like a snake into a narrow, barely passable, opening in the earth—not even on a childhood dare or to save his very life. Just the thought of getting stuck in a hole on the way to some unknown underground destination would generate a panicky sweat to his brow, palpitations to his heart, and paralysis to every muscle in his body. This incapacitating feature of the phobia impacted one of the critical periods of Adam Barnes' life, an experience that would transform him into the man he would become.

––––––––––––

As teenagers, the boys of the neighborhood had unfortunately progressed in their competing to battle with pellet guns and air rifles. Fully but naively aware of the potential dangers, fifteen-year-old Barnes and several friends commenced to play war games in the woods. Armed with copper spheres and lead pellet ammo, they stalked each other as prey amidst the ramparts of rock and across the tree-filled tracts of rolling terrain.

As one spring afternoon drew to a close, Barnes found himself maneuvered to a protected position behind a fallen log adjacent to a nearby stream. His friends had him pinned down from the limestone cliffs above. They held the high ground. Barnes could have escaped the pelting of pellets if only he were to slide into an open shaft in the rocks beneath the ridge of the cliff. The nook would have provided immediate refuge. However, this narrow channel, approximately two feet by two feet square, was a corridor of about twenty feet, tunneling under the fieldstone. It would be tight fitting even for his skinny body, tension-producing for his nerves, and way too long in the teen's imaginings.

Visions of a black bear hibernating in its lair or a raccoon guarding its burrow dominated the "newsflashes" in his mind. The immediate choices at hand were to crawl into the unknown or to make a run for it. To surrender and thus concede the contest was NOT considered. By rule, whoever got hit with a BB bullet was out of that round of play and at this late point in the day, loser of the whole game. Barnes hated to lose—at anything.

Incomprehensibly, Adam decided to attempt the escape route down the fissured passageway which led beneath the wall of rock. He twisted to lie on his back and entered the hole headfirst, pushing his gun forward with his extended fingers. Movement was slow as he shuffled along digging into the moist soil with his heels for propulsion. The natural tunnel had that musty odor of dampness. His face was turned upward and his arms were positioned ahead of his shoulders. He used his hands to inch his body onward, fingers groping for traction points along the way—a crack cleavage here, a ledge indentation there. When his hand fortuitously encountered a root, he pulled on it. It dislodged, rolling off the ledge onto his chest and bringing clumps of dirt down with it. "Would the ceiling collapse?" Barnes worried.

Then the "root" moved and slithered swiftly past Barnes' neck on the left beneath his head and beyond any further tactile sensation with his now rigidified body. The decision to withdraw was instantaneous. But execution of his hasty retreat had to wait until muscular rigor mortis eased up and abated.

Barnes could not see where the snake went. He was not looking ahead. He was pushing with his palms to propel himself in the opposing direction, back the way he had come. Going out sure went much faster than entering.

After a few quick breaths of fresh air, Barnes remembered why he had been in that crawl space in the first place. He rose up to check again on the positions of his playmates. As he peeked over the fallen trunk of timber, his right eye absorbed an instant stab of pain. He rolled flat to his back in recoil behind the tree barrier and peered straight up into the blue sky.

Clouds were swirling—swirling in his eye—and immediately the blue was gone. Only light filtered through an expanding sheet of opaqueness. A seeing eye was turning to blind.

CHAPTER 4

A SHEPHERD IN
THE SHADOWS

"**A**dam! You all right?" echoed from the cliff top.

Barnes yelled back, "No! You got me in the eye."

The friends scurried down to his aid immediately. Upon examination, all they could see was a residual red spot in the blue disk of the eye, the point of impact by the pellet with the colored iris. The playmates were devastated and panicky, but there was nothing they could do. The damage was done.

As dusk was fast approaching, they headed out of the woods. Barnes told his friends that he was all right and he could make it home alone. Clearly they were distraught over the resultant injury, choosing in a fit of frustration to dismantle their guns by wrapping them around tree trunks along the path. With such a tragic conclusion, no thrill of victory would be experienced on this day, only agony.

The offending projectile was nearly spent when it struck the eyeball from such a distance, since it did not penetrate the globe. Yet hemorrhaging within was severe enough that a murky vitreous veil curtained down to impair all vision in the right eye. As the sun dropped below the western ridge, the ability to distinguish light was sorely diminished. The duel of the day had resulted in a duality of the night, doubling the darkness, without and within.

As Barnes made his way along the terraced path which wound beneath the crest of the ridge, a simple prayer recurred consciously. "Lord, please help me, sinner that I am—and in advance, thanks."

The principles of "please" and "thank you" were hallmarks in the Barnes' home. "Please" before every request and "thanks" in everything (1 Thess. 5:18). Adam's mom was a devout Christian woman. Whether he felt like it or not, in everything he had been reared to say "please" and "thanks." That was the habit in the household. As an adolescent, Barnes, often times in trouble, would flash the prayer, "Lord, please...and thanks in advance." It was his spiritual shorthand.

Entering the basement of his house, Barnes seemed more fearful of the expected "I told you so" than of anything else. It never came. Only a sympathetic mother's embrace, a studied look, and an immediate rush to the emergency room of a local eye specialty hospital as a referral from the family's personal physician. The facility was aptly named The Shepherd's Hospital. The case was evaluated by the resident ophthalmologist on duty who determined that no surgery was warranted that night. However, with such a severe hemorrhage within the eyeball, the full extent of damage could not be assessed. So the haunting questions persisted. Would vision still be intact behind the bloody veil, or if not, would it ever be restored? Only time would tell.

Admission to the hospital came next with assignment to an isolated floor, quiet and far from the visitation traffic of other patients. Patches covering both eyes were applied with bandage tape. Then the staff nurses guided Barnes onto his bed and immobilized his head with sandbags. The prescribed treatment was total bed rest and time. Watch and wait! They would watch and Barnes would wait.

One of his mother's life verses from the Bible was Colossians 4:2: "Devote yourself to prayer and watch (keep alert) with an attitude of thanksgiving." Waiting without the ability of watching (seeing), Barnes "watched" by praying. Night and day were broken down into prayer watches. Jesus had asked His disciples to "watch and pray," but in the Garden of Gethsemane, they failed. Barnes was determined he would not fail. "Lord, please help me, and thanks in advance."

Barnes was not the only one praying. Immediate family, relatives across the country, and community friends all offered their supplications for the healing of this young man.

In the darkened world behind the patches from the very first night, Barnes experienced a strange spiritual Presence. He was unable to describe it with words, but it came as a personal embodiment of calming reassurance. "It will be what it will be—and you will never have to face it alone." Rather than curse the darkness, he chose to accept God's gift of an inner light.

Over the next few days, Barnes would not feel the Presence all the time, but he would surely know it. The Presence was becoming more personal. The relationship revolved around acknowledging Jesus of Nazareth as the Son of God and as the Lord of his life. Barnes had known Him as "Savior," but not as "Lord." Being a Christian believer encompassed a new and challenging understanding for Barnes. To believe was to obey and obeying meant one really believed. The believing who Jesus was and what He said was the easy part. The obeying of the Will of God as revealed in His Word, not just knowing it, would prove to be the harder aspect of faith. To this teenage boy, it may have boiled down to something as simple as "trust and obey." Adam Barnes was trusting in childlike faith, such truths as those depicted in the Bible story of Blind Bartimaeus and in the hymnal words of John Newton, "…was blind, but now I see…."

Whatever would happen in the days ahead would not change for Adam Barnes, but he would be changed. His awareness of the Presence of God was permanent. In the dark or in the light, in the wrong or in the right, in life and in death, he would never be alone. "And in advance, thanks be to God!"

After ten days of dark stillness, the patches were removed. A certain amount of emotional anxiety was present while the bandage sections were carefully loosened and lifted, one adhesive strip at a time. Most of the hemorrhagic debris in the inner chamber of the eyeball had resolved. Only a few "floating" remnants sailed the visual seas. Encouragingly, vision was still intact.

With an opthalmoscope, the doctor discovered only two pinhole-sized scars one millimeter outside the optic nerve's insertion into the retina. Permanent blindness had been averted, but just by that fraction. Yet the miracle was not in the near miss of damaging the optic disc; it came with an incredible regeneration of the lining of the retina.

In later consults, the medical specialists cautioned that due to some residual scarring of the lens, a post-traumatic cataract could develop sooner rather than later. Should that occur, surgery would be required to correct the cataract. That was the expected feature. What could not be explained was a supernormal improvement of both peripheral and night vision in the right eye. One technical explanation posited considered that the rods, the photosensitive nerve cells in the retina, had increased in numbers as the film layer was reformed. These added numbers could provide a potential elevation of the chemical, visual purple, which enhances the adaptability of the eye to low density light, thus improving night vision. No matter what the scientific reason, through the restorative process, Adam's right eye would seem to have gained an augmented acuity for seeing in the dark. To the teenager, that fact, not the ultimate cause, was all he needed to know. In his mind, the cause for his special sight was God.

Within two years, the doctor's cataract prediction came to fruition and surgery had to be performed. The new lens remarkably restored a quality of sight superior to the levels before the injury with another inexplicable enhancement. Contrary to expectations, Barnes' night sight appeared to light up the nighttime fields of view like peering through a night scope. Just the slightest flicker of luminosity allowed Barnes to differentiate surrounding objects in detail, though without specific color, just very defined hues of black and white.

What an astounding resolution to a tragic trauma. What a phenomenal finish, to take the near devastation of blindness and to transform it into the uncanny capacity to see more clearly and more confidently even among the shadows. "Thanks be to God!"

CHAPTER 5

CLOSING THE CLOSENESS DOOR

The traumatic episode with temporary blindness and the spiritual encounter with the Presence of God in that hospital room caused an about-face during the teen's rebellious march away from religious faith. At that point in time, Adam Barnes was a lonely boy, intentionally walking away from God. The same God who years earlier had taken his baby brother away from him!

When Adam was five, a year after his father had returned from overseas during World War II, the family membership was increased by one Dana William Barnes. The "prayed-for" brother with whom he could run and play, the long-awaited companion for doing boy's things had arrived. Barnes' older sister had her own friends and world, a girl's world in which little brother always seemed to get in the way. Adam and Dana would share the excitement of boys being boys. Climbing the apple tree, chasing the pet dog, kicking, catching, batting, and shooting balls together. Adam deeply loved his brother.

The date was April 7, the Monday after Easter 1947. Adam was harshly awakened by a piercing shriek that resonated throughout the whole one-story home. The cry had come from his mother.

Dana Barnes was unexplainably dead at the age of six months. Stumbling across the nursery bedroom, Adam unintentionally became a witness to the last gaze of his brother lying in the crib. The whole concept of death was a shock to a five-year-old's fragile psyche, but viewing the actual face of death of this beloved baby boy became a haunting image for the older brother.

The frequent, well-meaning references to his brother as now being "with God" were interpreted by a five-year-old as "God took him." Just when the bond between brothers was being formed, it was broken. God broke it by taking Dana away. Under the circumstances an immature child could hypothesize wrongly that if you love someone too much or more than you love God, then God will take them from you. And you will hurt.

What was the conscious or subconscious conclusion for Barnes as a boy? To avoid the eventual pain of intimate closeness, *don't get too close!* Then the loss of the loved cannot hurt you.

Adam Barnes learned and conditioned himself quickly. No one and no thing would ever get that close to him again. No god, no sibling, no acquaintance. The wall he erected around his heart was granite solid. On the outside he could appear affable and good-natured, even gregarious at times, but on the inside, behind the friendly façade, was the reserve of a lost and alone little boy. As a dauntless defender of the wall, no one was allowed even to approach.

Relationships with the opposite sex were mostly platonic through the teen years—no infatuations, no emotional crushes. The wall as constructed appeared impenetrable. He was unreceptive to romance. He felt safe in his unattached state. "He who runs alone, runs fastest." Dana's death contributed greatly to young Barnes turning out socially to be a somewhat tragic figure, content with just living the life of a likeable loner, yet never alone.

No one could reach him—until that knock at the door of his heart by the Shepherd, that touch of the Master's hand. An associated consequence of becoming a Christian believer was the progression toward dismantling Barnes' barrier to intimacy. The entryway in the wall had been cracked open ever so slightly. Someone now could enter in if they had the perseverance to probe the length and breadth of the wall until they came to the unlatched entrance; now open, but barely ajar.

One girl, a young woman to be more accurate, undaunted and undazzled by the enormity of the wall but intrigued by the person behind it, strode right up as if seeing no wall at all. At first she was a colleague; in time she became a confidant, a person with whom Adam could be himself. She was not looking for the door. Her infatuated heart belonged to another, but she could become a trusted friend for Barnes.

Claire Marshall was the staff nurse at the Jackson Mill Camp where Adam spent his summers during medical school. She was a recent graduate of Broaddus University School of Nursing and he, a rising second year med student at Duke. They were drawn to each other by their vocational interests in medicine and their faith-based desire to help the less fortunate in life: the underdogs, those the world tagged as losers, the lonely, the lost, the oppressed, the orphaned, and the needy.

Of course, the attraction from a male's perspective was the physical. Claire had a tanned, smooth complexion, tall slender stature and long blond hair braided into a single ponytail for summer comfort. She would have made the perfect poster girl for the Brothers Grimm as Rapunzel with her hair extending down to her waist in back. Her deep blue eyes accentuated her natural beauty like two brilliant sapphires arrayed beside a single diamond. She moved with such a graceful gait that she appeared like an American flag whipping in the wind—loose fitting little red top, flowing platinum white hair, and faded, flared blue jeans. Her father had nicknamed her Clairy when she was two. He called her his "Little Clairy Princess." The name stuck but the spelling changed to Clairee.

Clairee struggled as a teenager with another peer-inflicted title. She was a PK, a preacher's kid. Born in Louisville, Kentucky while her father was in seminary, she had grown up in the church. Her interest for nursing started at an early age in her grandfather's clinic. At age four she was given the task of taking patients back to their designated examining room. She learned charity and generosity from the physician she affectionately called "Papa Doc." Later in life she discovered the secret code her grandfather frequently used in his patient ledger detailing remuneration for treatment. The one that stood out was TPTP, "too poor to pay." No one was ever turned away for lack of funds. If Santa Claus had ever decided to be a doctor, the prototype would have been Papa Doc. He even had the jolly old laugh, the one "infection" he loved to share with his patients.

After a wearisome day of camp duties the staff counselors could relax away from the tedium, leaving the oversight of campers and cabins to the junior counselors. Following the playing of the Lord's Prayer over the loud speaker and "Taps" being bugled, staff co-ed fraternization was permitted in specific locations only—the laundry room, the craft house, and the dining hall.

Barnes and Marshall enjoyed slow dancing on the hardwood floors of the camp dispensary. The music source on those occasions was a small portable radio. Contemporary rock stations could be tuned in and out from stations in Chicago, Boston, even Charlotte, North Carolina.

Camp romances often progressed from platonic to personal as the days of summer raced toward fall. Not so for Clairee and Adam. They were just friends, good friends, company for each other. Clairee was seriously dating a graduate student from her hometown and Adam feigned dating a young woman back in Durham, but it was "nothing serious."

Many evenings when the covered wagon group was encamped at the lake, Nurse Marshall would ride out on horseback and sit on the hillside with or without Barnes during the Cong games. The entertainment value of this spectacle was simply in watching these young campers as they scampered up and down the valley, spooked by any motion on the paths or by any rustling in the weeds. The numerous flashlights blinking on and off amidst the fireflies presented a most unique fireworks display beneath the amphitheater canopy of stars.

After the campers were bedded down for the night, Adam and Clairee would sit beside the campfire and converse on topics which ranged from politics and theology through medicine, missionary endeavors, sports, and the war.

"What was it like to play at Duke's Cameron Indoor Stadium?" was Clairee's icebreaker after an icy moment of "politics."

"1960 to 1964," was Adam's short retort. He had not heard the question clearly.

"Did you know that my father played in college too? Football, that is. He was a quarterback."

"I didn't know that."

"Yes, in fact he played on the Appalachian College team that was unbeaten and unscored upon."

"You can't get any better than that," said Adam.

"It was the perfect season," she replied.

This innocuous conversation was Clairee's attempt to change the subject which just before had been the war. Their opinions had clashed or at least had constructively conflicted. On the issue of the Vietnam War, they had agreed to disagree without being disagreeable.

These two ardent acquaintances were a lot alike in spite of their differing assessments on *the war*. Their differences would not be allowed to reach a degree that would discourage a healthy friendship between them. From the day of camp orientation, an amicable relationship had continued to develop between the two.

The national rivalry of the day regarding the Vietnam War was divided into two groups, Hawks versus Doves. Claire Marshall was a Dove, an eternal advocate for peace. In her mind, war would always be the last resort.

Regarding Vietnam, Claire would never have chosen to fight this war having great sympathies for the South Vietnamese and the North Vietnamese—their people, not their politics. Her compassion was overwhelming in regards to this tragedy of civil strife and the concomitant injuries foisted upon the innocent. Terrorist tactics and collateral casualties were all the same to the one seeking to heal the harmed, those who, for no fault of the own, were being victimized by the impact of war.

Unlike the majority of that era's war dissenters, Claire could maintain a mature neutrality with her consistent criticism of the entity of *war*, while offering no room and no quarter to the political propagandists. She had little respect for those American protesters who seemed only to hate the United States' involvement in the war while condoning the rival, communist enemy's role. To her, both sides were in complicity with the destruction of human life. From her perspective one could condemn the consequences of war on both sides without aiding and assisting either side in the prolongation of the war. She was very prayerful about a negotiated peace settlement between the parties involved. She genuinely believed that such a settlement would save lives.

On that last point, Adam felt his friend was a bit naïve. He was a Hawk with certain qualifiers. Regarding the war in Southeast Asia, he believed that if the South Vietnamese people were not willing to make the sacrifices essential to establishing a free society for themselves, why should American soldiers be maimed or die on their behalf? Freedom is not free. There is a price.

Barnes would affirm that the history of the United States is a textbook of the struggles and self-sacrifices required to build a noble nation. Our country has sent its sons and daughters to foreign shores to provide the chance of freedom for the "unfree." Many heroically fought and died in this honorable quest. And they were doing it again in Vietnam.

However, Adam Barnes had a dilemma similar to the housewife who was quoted internationally saying, "I want us to get out of Vietnam, but I don't want us to give up."

Barnes' father had instilled the working rule that once you started a task, committed to it, promised to complete it, you never quit until the job was finished—no matter what.

For Claire Marshall, this summer was to be her final tour as the camp nurse. She loved the children. She had become quite adept at calming fears and wiping tears as she went about her business of health and wellness at Camp Jackson Mill. Come September she would be heading west to San Francisco to work in a neonatal care unit of the University of California School of Medicine Hospital. Far from her hills, her home, and her family, but she would be near to her male college friend, a newly hired sociology professor at Stanford. In the heart of anti-war country, she would search for a new way to serve the war-burdened children of the world.

CHAPTER 6

BASIC AND BASKETBALL

The first escalation of the Vietnam War regarding United States involvement might be considered to be 1961. President John F. Kennedy sent additional military advisers into the South. The North Vietnam Army (NVA) and the Vietcong (VC) insurgents were threatening the overthrow of the Saigon government. Democratic nationalism and international communism were the opposing ideologies. Some simplistically designated the conflict as a civil war. As a sixties college student, Barnes did not see it that way. In fact, he did not think much about the war at all, not even the draft.

During his medical school years at Duke, the war had barely been a mental distraction. Combat communiqués and brief bulletins in the news or clamorous campus attitudes in the quadrangles might invade his consciousness, but Adam was not war aware. His war philosophy could be summarized as follows: we will help those who are willing to help themselves!

Barnes would use the excuse of corruption among the politicians of the Saigon regime to support his basic tenet of non-involvement. Although he acknowledged that this corruption was alleged, he had to appreciate the reality that many of his contemporaries believed the reports of political patronage to be true and that they were disheartened by the accounts. Still the *war* was on the opposite side of the world; biochemistry was here and now.

Adam had been reared to support his country and those who fought for it. As a child of a wartime generation, he had learned well the principle of supporting the American soldier wherever the nation's leadership would send them. For that reason he did support the troops, now almost 500,000 in Vietnam. The father's military insights from the Normandy Beach sacrifices of World War II were so ingrained in the son that a special place in that hardened heart was carved out for those men (the 20 percent in Vietnam) who literally confronted the enemy day to day on the fields of battle. Adam reasoned that a physician could minister medical care to the combatants no matter how he felt about the war.

With his expedited pediatric internship almost completed, the once far and away became the here and now. The effectuation of President Johnson's medical call-up had reached its final stages.

On a midsummer Monday in 1968, the expected military orders arrived by telegram. Barnes contacted his cousin in the air force to decipher the abbreviations APO, FT. DIX, and RVN. The recently drafted Barnes was going to Vietnam. Surprise, surprise! First he would be trained at Fort Sam Houston in San Antonio for four weeks and then sent to the Republic of Vietnam. (Dwight Eisenhower's first duty station was Fort Sam in 1915. He hated war too.)

The traditional basic course for other army inductees was eight weeks. Barnes thought that someone at a higher pay grade must have surmised that physicians did not need eight weeks. Therefore, medical officers were assigned to the four-week "speed reading" version. Within days, Barnes was questioning the reasoning behind the length of training reduction. This was definitely a matter for reconsideration he speculated.

The mold of a military "route-stepper" was a good fit for the Army Medical Corps. Considering the disorderly displays in the parade quadrangle, the marching techniques of the medical docs confirmed the moniker. Route-stepper was a most appropriate title. On the drill field this contingent of physicians was not too coordinated as a company unit. Verbal commands were corrupted into Keystone Cop chaos. Even the commanding general would exit the viewing veranda when he witnessed such confusion. Fortunately, these medical officers would not be called upon to carry out much precision, close order drill in the aid stations of Vietnam.

Upon arrival at Fort Sam, Adam Barnes was surprised to cross paths with a basketball rival from the University of North Carolina (UNC). His name was Doctor Brian Jenner, now a drafted dentist. He had played forward for Coach Dean Smith in his first few seasons which made him a court contemporary with Barnes for two years. Barnes was starting guard both as a freshman and as a varsity team member of the Duke University Blue Devils. As Coach Vic Bubas' first full recruiting class in 1960, these players had never lost to the UNC Tar Heels through ten games over a four-year career. The Duke–UNC rivalry was one of the most renown athletic competitions along "Tobacco Road" in the Atlantic Coast Conference. This cross-county competition (only eight miles separated the two campuses), in athletics as well as academics, spread to encompass the whole state. Barnes considered it an astounding accomplishment to be one of only a handful of Duke basketball players who could say they were "undefeated and still champions" against UNC for his entire college career.

During one of the limited breaks from training, Barnes and Jenner went over to the post gym to shoot some basketball. They were instantly recruited into a pick-up game challenge against some of the base gym rats. On the hardwood that day, the two ex-collegians were the superior talents, seeming to have not lost a step. What a rare sight to see two former arch enemies from Duke and Carolina playing on the same team.

Tom Edwards, special services coach of the army team had been sitting on the sidelines observing the play of the two doctors. When the games were over, he approached Barnes and Jenner to question them about their background in basketball. The coach had visions of enhancing his army post team with these former collegiate round-ballers. He asked for permission to make an inquiry about a possible change of orders for both.

The army team had not been very successful, much less competitive, in the military league. Fort Sam was repeatedly being drubbed by the air force teams, especially the one from nearby Lackland Air Force Base (AFB).

Both Jenner and Barnes were curious about the possibility of such a reassignment but would not campaign for such a move. Barnes chose to leave it in God's hands and there it would stay. What will be will be—the rice paddies of Vietnam or the grassy plains of Texas.

As was the routine of many medical officers, that evening they headed over to the Lackland AFB training annex. The air force officers' club was a first-class restaurant with food that surpassed the army's cuisine offerings. Coach Edwards had told Barnes and Jenner that his team was scrimmaging against the air force team that night. He had encouraged them to check out the competition. After dinner they took their seats in the gym. Barnes and Jenner leaned back against the empty bleachers and casually glanced at the two teams warming up. First a double-take glance; then a long, lingering look by Barnes. He turned to Jenner. "I hate that guy!"

Jenner came back. "Which one?"

"The tall one. He's Coy Thornton."

As the air force center barked profanity after profanity at his teammates, Jenner responded, "Yep, that's Coy Boy! I played my sophomore year with him at Carolina when he was a senior. It looks like he never got Coach Smith's adage that 'you don't have to cuss to communicate effectively.'"

"Coach Smith said that?" Barnes asked with a quizzical glance.

"Sure did. I didn't know Thornton was down here. Why do you hate him?"

Barnes raised his left hand, pointing his index finger to a small crescent-shaped scar beneath his left eyelid. "He gave me this my freshman year."

Barnes recalled the infamous Duke-UNC brawl game of 1961. He related how the preliminary freshman game got out of hand also. It ended up with three Duke scrub players playing against the final three eligible players who had dressed out for Carolina. All the rest of the UNC team had fouled out.

Duke had won the game handily, but Adam was not in the stadium for the final buzzer. He had been taken to the hospital with a tripod fracture of his left cheek. Early in the second half, Barnes had gotten around the man guarding him and was driving for an open lay-up. As he drove down the lane, Thornton came from the blind side leaping toward the rim. He took Barnes out like a flying WWF wrestler executing an elbow drop off the top rope. The force was so fierce that it fractured the eye socket bones in three places.

Barnes would remember that cheap shot every time he looked in the mirror, every time he shaved and every time he pulled on the Duke jersey to play UNC at home or away. That incident became a motivational memory to "kill" Carolina in every rivalry game over the next three varsity seasons. On the hardwood, his record against the Tar Heels was untarnished.

Barnes had known Thornton, a New York City native, from summer basketball camps prior to his freshman year. Coy Thornton had originally signed a letter of intent to play for Duke but changed his mind during late summer. His father had graduated from UNC which may have played a part in the switch. But the word on the street was that Thornton loved the party atmosphere of Chapel Hill. He was wined and dined with Carolina beauties and the rest was history. When in the course of competition between UNC and Duke, an athlete chooses one of these institutions over the other, a spark of animosity is fanned into the eternal flame of *the rivalry*. The flame gets hotter and more *blue*.

Jenner and Barnes stayed only for the first half of the army–air force scrimmage. The AFB team with Thornton, a mountainous man in the middle, controlled every aspect of the game against the troopers from Fort Sam. Because of his size the Lackland pivot man was a dominant force in the paint, both offensively and defensively.

No army player was permitted an unmolested, uncontested lay-up. Either the ball would get blocked or the body of the shooter would get blocked. No one got an open lay-up without paying a physical price. Thornton was the enforcer. His added poundage intimidated every opponent who approached the basket rim. His long arms menaced every shot like an octopus. After one crushing block which drove the Fort Sam player into the goal support, Barnes had seen enough. It was time to go. He was emitting smoke and he was not a smoker.

As they walked to the car, Jenner shared a campus rumor circulating around Chapel Hill as to how Thornton ended up in the air force. Apparently Coy Boy had tried to beat the draft when he came out of college. He had a very ingenious plan. Army regulations stated that no recruit six foot eight inches or taller could be inducted into the service due to uniform and bedding restrictions. Coy Thornton was reportedly six foot eight, though heights were often inflated in the official team program as a means of intimidation. He had studied the science of the human skeleton and was counting on the fact that a person was at his tallest in the morning after all the discs in the spine had recouped their shape after a period of restfulness in the prone position. Thornton decided to spend the night in a motel near the recruiting station where he was scheduled to take his physical. He surmised that he would bypass the effects of gravity by sleeping nearby. Just a brief walk across the street and he expected to measure out at six feet eight inches resulting in his rejection—failure to pass the height limitation, a 4F.

On that fateful day, the measuring bar was raised inch by inch to the level of six feet seven and three quarter inches. Thornton passed his physical. His draft eligibility for the army was confirmed. "The best laid plans of mice and men…." That very same afternoon, Coy Thornton enlisted in the air force and eventually was assigned to the Training Annex at Lackland.

———————

The next morning after the army–air force scrimmage, there was a message for Barnes to contact Major Edwards. At that meeting he was informed that because his duty orders were for Vietnam, only a general had the authority to countermand a war zone assignment. It could happen with the major's recommendation if Barnes requested the change personally.

What a tantalizing choice for Barnes. Play basketball and teach medicine in Texas or go to Vietnam and fight. What a dilemma. He agonized over the question of cowardice if he chose to stay in the states. He was reminded of the men who had fled over the border to Canada to avoid the draft instead of going to prison for two years because of their conscientious opposition to the war. One may have been a coward; the other was worthy of respect. As a person who had accepted the draft, those choices were not a part of Barnes' predicament.

Just when he had almost been persuaded to stay, for the opportunity of inflicting some more Blue Devil retribution on his Tar Heel nemesis, Barnes changed his mind. If the new duty assignment had come as a natural occurrence, he probably would have considered it, but he could not bring himself to make such a request for special treatment just to play basketball. He would always have doubts about whether he just wanted to sit out the war safely in the States.

Destiny was directing him to Vietnam. He had trusted God with that decision and so it would be. But deep down, Adam hoped his spiritual interpretation of the dilemma was right. *Vietnam was not a game. It was a war!*

CHAPTER 7

A FIRST AT BEING LAST

In the military, good-natured competition can enhance the esprit de corps while pushing the trainees to be the best they can be. On the other hand, a cutthroat approach to competing can be detrimental. Those who had experienced the world of sports seemed better suited to the discipline required to be successful.

"All discipline for the moment seems not to be joyful, but sorrowful; yet to those who have been trained by it, afterwards it yields good fruit." (Heb. 12:11)

Adam Barnes and Brian Jenner thrived in one-on-one and group competitive endeavors. The compulsory training exercises like the obstacle course and the map reading courses were just such opportunities. These proved to be peaceful diversions in preparation for the unmerciful perversion of war.

The night obstacle course turned out to be a two-man race between these ACC school rivals. No one else in their group was even in the picture. The objective was, while crawling on one's belly, to negotiate the open field of dirt furrows, barbed wires, explosive simulations, and tracer bullets which brightly bedeviled the darkness.

In Barnes' group, against the backdrop of a stifling night, a single shout of alarm was an additional motivation for speed. Someone down the line yelled, "There's a rattlesnake in the trench!" No official command to start was heard, but the race was on. Barnes was the first to "snake" his slender frame to the other side. The reason: his crippling and incapacitating fear of snakes, all kinds, from his childhood. He was highly energized to get out of that trench as fast as he could and as far away as he could.

Unfortunately since no command to start had ever been given, the unit was reassembled in the starting ditch. In single file they were spaced behind the berm of dirt so that the exercise could be repeated. This time when Barnes reached the finishing barrier, he looked to his side like a 100-yard-dash man might to see who was second. On his right he glimpsed Jenner touching in at the same time. A rare tie between the two friendly rivals.

The scuttlebutt on the bus ride back was that the rattle-snake-induced practice heat had been clocked at a record-setting pace for doctor recruits at Fort Sam. Every participant, first to last, had allegedly completed the course under the previous best time held for the past decade.

For the day map reading course these military neophytes were divided into multiple teams of four. Barnes and Jenner ended up on the same team. For this task each member of the foursome had a specified function: map reader, compass sighter, direction marker, or stride pacer. Each team was given a fixed compass co-ordinate (azimuth) which would lead to the location of a designated marker on a boundary fence miles away. The tract of land was made up of varying surface features and was full of a variety of natural obstacles like trees and boulders. This map-reading course was to be completed in two hours, out and back, just in time for lunch.

The practicum effort for some would turn out to be ill-fated. As noon drew near and the midday sun beamed down more harshly, the team of Barnes, Jenner, Smith, a heavyset dermatologist from Florida and Johnson, a psychiatrist from New Jersey, found themselves last. They had failed to find even the target fence.

Captain Barnes surmised what could be the problem but was too abashed to reveal his secret eye condition. He was the compass man on the team. His sighting errors could have been explained by the distorting floaters in his eye from his accident. One misaligned reading of the compass could shift the line of course off incrementally, thus compounding the error with each of the multiple visual calculations. The team eventually was traveling on a parallel with the fence rather than progressing toward a point of intersection.

Then without warning, out of the overhead sun dropped a Huey helicopter. Its on-station arrival was quickly followed by two jeeps raising dust as they were driven to the rescue. What was the rationale for this maximum show of responsiveness?

In the previous basic training class of doctors two weeks earlier, an army physician with orders to go to Vietnam had gotten "lost"—just outside the reserve, onto Interstate 35, south to Laredo and over the border into Mexico. He had taken this dishonorable approach to avoid active duty in Vietnam while participating in the day map reading exercises.

It was never intimated that Barnes and his colleagues were attempting a similar run to the border, but clearly the training staff was concerned about the possibility of another desertion, thus the need for a helicopter and two jeeps.

For the two highly competitive former athletes, the greater humiliation was not the suspicion of desertion, but rather the show of derision from the other trainees as this "lost team" was led into the mess hall last. They were the only quartet who failed to complete the compass course.

In order not to fail a second time, which would result in having to repeat another four weeks of basic training, the night map reading format was researched and planned by Jenner. After several recon calls and interviews with those who had already completed the night course, the team devised a game plan to insure success. In truth this strategy would defeat the whole purpose of the night map training experience. Jenner read the following recommendations he had gleaned:

When the bus lets the team off at your particular interval on the road, sight the assigned compass reading and start running as fast as you can along the stipulated azimuthal angle. It will still be light as you run toward the setting sun. Soon you will encounter a fence. Go either right or left until you find a stake along the fence line. It will give you a return compass direction. Sight it and start running as fast as you can until darkness overtakes you. Then walk fast on the same line listening for the mechanical hum of an engine that powers an isolated water-well pump, the only rig in the area. The checkpoint for every team is right in front of that well.

No one asked where Jenner got his information. Or how much it might have cost. The bus dropped the four men off, and after a brief direction-finding orientation with the compass, this time by Jenner, away they ran. The shortest distance between two points is a straight line and the four docs cut a four-lane path through shrubs, small trees, and all forms of underbrush to their appointed destination, the fence. Nothing could stop them.

The cattle fence appeared through the trees. Thirty feet to the right and there the peg rose out of the ground with the return directional setting written on the back.

It was still light, so with even greater boldness and reckless abandon, off they sprinted until dusk began to settle in. Surprisingly, it got dark quick! Still they jogged on confidently, only tuning in to their sense of hearing to guide them through the murky shadows. Barnes was confident because of his special night vision. He had the vision of an owl, distinguishing objects in the dark before anyone else was able. This aptitude was intentionally kept a secret from his comrades who naturally would attribute Adam's swift and accurate negotiation of the terrain to his athletic agility.

As the "Four Musketeers" plowed into the pitch black night, suddenly there were only three. Doctor Bob Smith had gone down as they were traversing a washed out ravine. Taking a long, leaping stride, his left foot had sunk into a prairie dog hole causing his ankle to twist severely. It was not broken but he now was disabled and incapable of rapid mobility. Running for him was out of the question.

Up to that point the team had not encountered any of the patrols that were supposed to be cruising the course to capture any behind-the-lines soldiers. Being captured or surrendering for the purpose of getting Smith some help would mean failure and more embarrassment. Smith expressed a desire to struggle on even if the team might come in last again. At the least, they would have completed the course.

Brian Jenner was frustrated by the delay, incensed at the possibility of being last again. He offered another plan.

"I'm going to run on ahead. I refuse to come in last. When I get to the check-in station, I'll send them back to help you."

Without any discussion he disappeared into the dark at a full-speed sprint, imaginary fumes flaring from his ears.

After tightening Smith's boot, Barnes and Johnson helped their fallen colleague to his feet. Placing his arms around their shoulders, Smith in the middle, they limped off still listening intently for the mechanical cadence of a generator. Traveling over this intensely rugged ground became most laborious, as Smith was a large man. They were like three men tied together in a simulated three-legged race, but unable to run. They were forced to decelerate to a rambling gait; then, a dragging crawl.

Within seconds of the threesome getting started again, they heard a tremendous "thud" ahead in the moonless blackness. Upon arriving in the clearing close to where they heard the sound, Barnes visually detected Jenner lying on the ground, gasping for breath.

"What happened?" Johnson whispered.

Jenner slowly got to his feet, still bent over. Breathlessly, he attempted an explanation.

"I was jogging…through the murk…listening for the sound of the well pump and…a twinge of guilt hit me so I turned my head to hear if you all were coming…then, *wham*, my chest struck something straight on…hard. It knocked the wind right out of me and I buckled on my butt backward, flat out.

"At first I thought I had run into the spare tire on the back of a patrol jeep, but while I was lying on the ground, it backed over me…and stomped on my leg twice. It was then I realized I had rear-ended some stupid sleeping cow. A Texas Longhorn or something!"

With that final comment, everyone began stifling a laugh. Even Jenner could not fail to see the humor in his own predicament. Laughter truly was a good medicine and Smith seemed to be benefiting from the break with a renewed strength in his sprained ankle and less pain.

From that point the team stayed together, just walking and listening—with Barnes "watching" and listening.

At first, they heard just a distant mechanical murmur. Then, a more distinct cyclic sound like a drilling rig. The informant had been correct about the mysterious pump. As the group approached the checkpoint tent, a ray of light escaped the door flap. It was just enough illumination for the owl to make out the derrick towering above and just behind the tent. The Fearsome Foursome signed in. Night map reading mission accomplished. Last practice game over. Soon the real season would begin.

But Vietnam was not a game. It was a war.

The final days of basic training passed rapidly without incident. All requirements of field medicine, military protocol, and standard administration were completed.

Weekend leave was granted at the conclusion of orientation so each physician could return home to visit family before being shipped overseas. Not every soldier took advantage of this opportunity, but Barnes did. He drove all through the night for that one last visit with his parents, and the younger brother born several years after Dana died.

Monday morning came too quickly. Adam's mother had sent her husband off to war and now she was sending her son. Lifting off the flattened mountaintop of the Charleston airport and banking over the Kanawha River, Joplin Hollow, and his home, Barnes experienced a solemn moment of remembrance and farewell.

The commercial flight headed west. Barnes had received new orders while at Fort Sam. Travis Air Force Base near Oakland, California, became his point of overseas departure. The change of embarkation was much to Barnes' liking. Claire Marshall still lived in San Francisco.

CHAPTER 8

LEAVING ONE'S HEART IN SAN FRANCISCO

Three years had passed since Adam and Claire had seen each other. Correspondence had been intermittent after that final summer campfire.

Claire had lived in San Francisco all this time developing a special fondness for pediatric public health and preventive medicine. Twice a week she assisted physicians at a free health clinic in Berkley working primarily with destitute families and children.

These community experiences were her mission field. Her faith drew her there; her passion to be a home missionary kept her coming back. As these children tugged at her apron strings, they tugged deeper at her heart strings.

Absence was working its magic on Adam's heart in another way. Out of the treasured memories of Claire at Jackson's Mill summer camp, vague feelings of affection were bubbling in his imaginings. Deep-felt desire was stirring from a source which Barnes had squelched many times before. They were indelibly there, but what were these emotions? Was it love? And why now? These were the poignant musings dancing across his mind.

Upon arriving in the cable car capital, Barnes found Claire's phone number in the directory and made a call. She was excited about his present arrival but saddened when he told her about his future destination.

Barnes went to pick up Claire at her apartment at North Beach. As she opened the door, he was overwhelmed in his senses. Her greeting voice was entrancing as always. Though Adam was not a drinking man, he could get intoxicated by the mere lavender fragrance emitting from Claire's hair. When accompanied by the gentle graze of her fingers on his bare forearm, he was sensuously enthralled. However, it was a flicker of light on her caressing left hand that abruptly sobered the moment of reunion.

Claire's hand was adorned with a ring—a diamond ring. The explanation came instantly as Claire discerned the reason for Adam's prolonged stare at the brilliance of the stone. She was engaged. She was now pledged to marry the same man she had been dating that last summer at camp; he was now working on his doctorate at Stanford. They had set no specific date for the wedding but leaned toward a time after he completed his dissertation work.

At first glimpse of Claire's banded hand, Barnes felt a pang in the pit of his stomach, a punch to his solar plexus. Then the pain of disappointment began to swell like a wave welling up just before it crashes onto the sandy shore.

Instinctively, Adam suppressed hard his emotions behind the barrier wall. She was betrothed and that was a state Barnes had been raised to honor. Friendship was all he should expect in their relationship. That infatuating thrill he had been experiencing in anticipation of this moment was exhaled away. A stab, a gasp and it was gone. Only the dull "hurt ache" of bruised feelings lingered. It too would pass in four to six weeks like any other bruised muscle, so he thought.

During dinner at a marina restaurant on Fisherman's Wharf,

the two reminisced about the summer days spent in the hills and vales of West Virginia. Claire led the conversation, focusing on her work. Barnes listened well, trying outwardly but awkwardly to display happiness for her. She was sensitive to the soldier side of Barnes. No discussion of the war or politics, like they used to do, would be appropriate.

Claire sensed that the news of her engagement had shocked and hurt Barnes. She could read it in his eyes but was puzzled by the stoicism in his demeanor. She even would have welcomed some words of challenge. Deep down Claire desired another response from her friend, but the timing of this reunion was so sudden and unexpected.

To ease some of the tension, Claire shared about a new project she had taken on. She was aware of a need for a public health nurse at an orphanage in Oakland. These were Vietnamese children, offspring of interracial encounters in the war zone. Orphans occupied a special place in the inner recesses of Claire's heart, since her own father had been, in essence, orphaned.

(During the Depression, her grandfather chose to leave and took his oldest boy with him. Her father and his older sister were left behind with relatives since his mother had died giving birth to him. Claire's dad had a hard life as an orphan and never was able to put down roots until he was invited into the home of Papa Doc and Momma Ila. These became the only grandparents on her daddy's side that she ever knew. Loving and nurturing orphaned kids had become a way for her to honor her grandparents for what they had done for her father.)

Just then the band at the restaurant began to play. Several couples made their way to the open-air dance pier beside the bay. The music was slow and inviting.

"One last dance?" Adam rose from his chair, hand extended.

"You were my favorite dancing partner," Claire replied as Barnes pulled her seat back.

The orchestra was playing an arrangement of "Cherish" made popular by the band, The Association. Barnes clearly would *not* "be the one to share her dreams," and he knew it. The door in the wall was closing.

After one dance the two friends strolled around the marina dock, then up the avenue inclines toward Telegraph Hill. At the duplex doorstep Barnes cradled Claire's face in his palms, leaned down, and tenderly kissed her forehead. With a gentle stroke of her hair which released a faint scent of lavender, Adam whispered, "Be blessed and be happy."

As he descended the steps to the sidewalk, Claire called softly, "Adam."

He stopped and turned back.

"I'll be thinking of you tomorrow." She paused and said, "No. I'll be praying for you."

Adam acknowledged her with a grateful nod. Claire's eyes were glistening in the moonlight. A tear caressed her cheek. But Adam could not see it. He was gone. His mind had made the turn along with his physical torso, even though the eyes of his heart were longingly looking back.

Barnes' flight was at 0600 hours. Claire had the first shift in the morning at the hospital, yet before leaving her apartment she fulfilled her promise of prayer. Soon she would be lifting the blinds to illumine her ward and preparing medications for her tiny tot patients. Barnes would be racing after darkness through Alaska north and then dropping south along the globe's curvature. This elliptical course would take him across the North Pacific, down to Japan and on to Southeast Asia.

As the commercial transport crossed over the South China Sea and landed at the Bien Hoa Air Base, there was noted a serious silence onboard the aircraft, almost funereal. In an instant the calm was shattered by the whine of jet engines powering down and the whirring of chopper blades powering up.

When the seal of the aircraft door was broken, the subtle sounds of a war welcomed the replacement troops as they unbuckled their seat belts. A sudden gust of dust greeted each serviceman as he exited the cabin. Day one toward DEROS had begun; three hundred sixty-four days to go.

It was a lot like going to summer camp at an old Civilian Conservation Corps project of the Roosevelt era. The barracks were wooden buildings with bunk beds lining the walls, head to foot. Space was at a premium.

After the initial sign-in, the new arrivals were furnished with basic issue items: green fatigues, green canvas boots, the ever crucial canteen, helmet and liner, and an M16 automatic rifle. Officers were supposed to receive a .45-caliber pistol, but for some unknown reason Barnes was issued the rifle instead. The standard admonitions were expressed about maintaining one's weapon and one's hydration. Both could mean the difference in survival.

Each man's equipment was to be stowed in a coarse canvas duffel bag. Along with his essentials, Barnes had brought a number of basic medical books, the weight of which proved quite heavy to tote all over Vietnam. Fortunately Barnes was physically fit for the task of carrying this extra load.

In the orientation sessions the soldiers were frequently re-minded to be prepared to leave for their specific duty assignment at any time, including the middle of the night. Since the administrative process was 24–7, each man was to be dressed, packed, and ready to go at all hours of the day or night.

Sure enough, the call for Captain Barnes was in the early morning hours of darkness. A tap on the bottom of his boot awakened him from a light slumber. Sleeping in one's shoes on top of the blankets was commonplace. Barnes' bunk was just inside the screen door. He was on top; Brian Jenner was on the bottom. Not a word was spoken. No light was ever turned on. Trying to balance a helmet and liner with a rifle and a full duffel bag slung over the shoulder was quite a feat in the dark, especially if trying to keep from waking others up.

Both men had been assigned to the First Air Cavalry Division (CAV), proudly referred to as the First Team. Following their military guide into the dawn, they zigzagged to a nearby airstrip where a C-130 transport was revving its propellers waiting to take off. As they boarded, Barnes counted thirty other soldiers already buckled in along the sides, duffel bags positioned between their legs. The ramp floor lifted shut behind them and within seconds they were airborne, heading north.

Fixed-wing flight was not one of Barnes' favorite pastimes. At this point he was having real hesitations about his assignment to an air mobile unit, considering his inherent fear of the turbulence associated with flying. He was army, not air force. If he was going to die, his choice would be to die on the ground at the mercy of his own feet, not free-falling from the sky at the mercy of some flying machine.

In regards to flying, he was *not* a daring young man. He

prayed, "Lord, please help me, and thanks I bring in advance."

The early dawn sun could be seen filtering its rays through the porthole of the fuselage door and its gun turret slits. Midmorning, as the heat was rising with the day's ration of dust, the plane landed. As the men disembarked, supplies were loaded on in their place. In an instant the C-130 "cargo" plane was off the ground again, leaving behind a band of thirty-two soldiers standing silently on the metal mesh tarmac dressed in clean, green fatigues.

On the other side of this airstrip was a Chinook helicopter sitting on an asphalt pad. Barnes and Jenner were separated from half of their group and directed to board the large chopper. Walking across the heat radiating runway, Barnes felt like he was aspirating asphalt. The oily smell mixed with an atmosphere of truck petroleum vapors and spilt diesel fumes nauseated the uninitiated. Sixteen men stayed and sixteen men were heading farther north.

It was becoming a chore for Barnes to lug his book-laden bag at every transfer. Sweat began to streak through his T-shirt onto his uniform. This chopper ride was much shorter. Every flight farther upcountry was bringing them closer and closer to the demilitarized zone (DMZ) between South Vietnam and North Vietnam. Barnes often thought to himself, "Four weeks of basic, and the fifth week I'm on the DMZ. What's wrong with this picture?"

It was about mid-afternoon when the final "hitch-hopping" ride for Jenner and Barnes took place. A medical evacuation aircraft (MEDEVAC) Huey helicopter returning to An Khe would transport them on the final leg of their journey.

By this final flight Barnes had adapted somewhat to flying, like the second and third runs on a roller coaster. After the first round a person comes to know what to anticipate. Traveling in helicopters turned out to be much easier for him than traversing the skies in a fixed-wing craft. God was answering Barnes' prayer.

The trick was imagination. Barnes would envision a mental picture of God reaching down and holding the helicopter from the top prop, His hand as a tether being invisible to passengers and pilots inside. The conscious imagining coupled with the natural aerodynamics of a helicopter seemed to give Barnes confidence in flight. The turbulent drops were absent. The only time those stomach-in-the-throat sensations could occur would be while spiraling straight down over some remote landing zone (LZ) to avoid enemy fire. Barnes hoped he would not be doing that.

An Khe was experiencing the end of the monsoon season. Rain and red clay did not mix well with new boots and clean uniforms. The sleeves initially were rolled up as per regulation. But at the earliest possible moment stripping to just an army-green T-shirt was preferred. Everyone was equal while wearing just a T-shirt; no rank, just a brother in battle.

Some of the CAV's major fighting was coming to a close in the northern provinces after the Tet Offensive. Rumor was that the First Team would be relocating south in just a few weeks. Barnes and Jenner were arriving just in time to move again.

CHAPTER 9

A MISSED OPPORTUNITY TO END THE WAR

Wisps of steam caused by a late afternoon shower were rising as the chopper approached An Khe headquarters. Cool rain encountering the parched clay made Barnes aware of his thirst. Out came the near-empty canteen again.

The Huey helicopter was flying at a higher altitude during the final leg of deployment for Barnes and Jenner—not because of any elevated terrain but to stay out of range of sniper fire by an AK-47 rifle. No pilot took chances with his cargo or his passengers on simple transport hops.

Barnes' body was fatigued by the heat, but his mind was on full alert. The Tet Offensive by the enemy had made everyone more cautious. Tet had reinforced the old sport adage: never take an opponent lightly, no matter how superior you are or think you are.

After Tet, public opinion about the war, as communicated by the media, was beginning to have an impact on the campus climate at home. Most people were being influenced by what they read in newspapers or saw on television. From these public inputs regarding the war, Barnes expected the frustration of a stalemate between two competing forces in Vietnam. The image of fighting a losing battle with one hand tied behind the back was not appealing. It was discouraging, especially to an athlete who was trained always to give total effort to win, not just play for a tie.

What Barnes observed as a first impression while he went deeper in-country was an encouraging carriage of confidence, especially in the pilots...later evident in the soldiers of the First Air Cavalry Division. Tet had tested these men ferociously, but they had survived the test; bent but not broken, to use a football analogy.

When he knew he was Vietnam-bound, Barnes had studied accounts of the Tet Offensive on his own. While playing college basketball, he had the habit of taking written notes during every scouting report. It helped him remember and concentrate on the weaknesses of the opponent, to stay focused in the game. He could use the edge, especially against the more gifted players he would be assigned to guard. Any knowledge of offensive tendencies by the enemy would provide a defensive advantage.

When Barnes arrived near the DMZ, it was only his fifth week in the army. He had already presumed that Tet had changed the war. It should have been for the better, but it turned out for the worse. Instead of a Victory in Vietnam Day with accelerated steps toward resolution, it seemed to set in motion processes for prolongation. From Barnes' perspective an opportunity for a negotiated settlement was squandered away—not in Saigon but in Washington, D.C.

The rival was reeling. What a waste it seemed to Barnes to let the enemy recover to fight again. The best athletic teams had a "killer instinct" to end a contest against a staggering opponent. It looked to him that the U.S. was lacking that instinct in this war. Killer-instinctive behavior would appear to be a dichotomy for a "do no harm" (Hippocratic oath) physician like Barnes.

However, Vietnam was not a game. Was it not a war either?

The Tet Offensive presented a turning point in the military conflict, but not all observers interpreted it in the same way. The Viet Cong guerrillas, with the assistance of the NVA, had struck all over the country with multiple surprise attacks. A key aspect of their strategy was the hope that South Vietnamese villagers would rise up and welcome them as liberators. That did not happen! To the contrary, in less than a month of fierce fighting—punching and counterpunching—these communist insurgents were soundly defeated. The U.S.-backed coalition's defensive stands and counterattacks severely decimated the effective fighting force of the enemy units. The Viet Cong bore the brunt of these confrontations with the Americans. By most criteria (body counts, enemy surrenders, land control) they were emphatically defeated.

No military victory over the allied soldiers took place. Granted, some battles were lost and some moments were quite dire, but by any standard of war, the soldiers from the United States and its allies, the Australians, the Koreans et al. were still undefeated when the smoke of battle cleared across the country…winning the war could begin the peace!

Across the ocean a different "stand" was taking place. Media titans, Washington bureaucrats, and propaganda-naïve politicians were impacting the perception of the war and Tet. News commentator C.K. Walters of the CBC network and Senator Fulton Bright had publicly insinuated that the war could not be won. Their journalistic approach was subtle, slick, and safe. Their use of legalese language distorted the interpretation of the war with phrases like, "maybe we cannot win!" If challenged, they would hide behind the word "maybe" and then slink away in retreat to statements that emphasized that the South Vietnamese had to "win their own war. The U.S. Army cannot do it for them." Half truths served to confuse the American people who understood self-sacrifice from their own historical perspectives.

During his presidency, Dwight Eisenhower had articulated the goal of America's involvement in the Far East: prevention of Vietnam falling into the hands of totalitarian communism. His "domino" concept was supported by many. Should Indochina fall, the rest of Southeast Asia would collapse very quickly like a row of dominos. Terrorism from within and tyranny from without would hasten the fall.

Complicating the whole picture in Vietnam was the Diem government which was functioning in disorganized, inefficient, and corrupt ways. Repression did exist; and amidst the populace, a growing unpopularity was festering along with a growing sense of insecurity.

After the Tet Offensive and the devastating defeat of the insurgents, an enormous opportunity existed to negotiate a valid peace agreement. A successful resolution of the two Vietnams' problem seemed a possibility, even if not an ideal one. The world united, standing against both the communist technique of guerrilla warfare and the tactic of local terrorism could exert enormous pressure toward peace.

Ideally, the birth of a free and democratic nation would appear to be a benefit for all the freedom-starved countries in the region; and furthermore, the potential undoubtedly existed there. The world had seen the restoration of Germany and Japan to amazing heights following their individual field of battle defeats. Militarily winning the war to start the peace (win-win) seemed to Barnes always to be better than stopping the war prematurely to negotiate some inconclusive settlement (win-lose).

In addition, Barnes simplistically wondered how anyone could miss the distinctions between the rival ideologies of a democratically "free" society and a socialistically "slave" society. From which were people attempting to escape and to which were people immigrating en masse: East Germany or West Germany, North Korea or South Korea, Red China or Nationalist Taiwan, Cuba or Costa Rico, the USSR or the USA? Such a choice was easily confirmed by statistical facts and a no-brainer for Barnes. Freedom first, foremost, and forever!

Captain Adam Barnes and his medical colleagues had been deposited into a war that combatively should have been over. The allies had withstood the major impetus of the enemy and had emerged victorious, having held back from using the awesomeness of their arsenal of nuclear weapons. Now they had the distinct attainability of securing and returning the landscape to the very villagers they had come to help and to save for freedom.

The "Chieu Hoi" (I surrender) program of amnesty and rehabilitation could be the new focus. The Free World unified on this issue of the restoration of a war-torn country would be essential—a necessity of paramount importance!

Unfortunately the "back-home" isolationists and pacifists did not recognize this opportunity for what it was. On one hand, the military war (actual physical combat) was over. On the other hand, a new warfare was on the horizon. A propagandistic war was the order of the day. The tyranny of untruth used words as weapons. Winning and losing depended upon whom you believed. The result was that destruction and death would continue as an affliction on the land for all the wrong reasons. The Vietnam War should have been ended after the Tet defeat. Why did it not? This question was most disconcerting to Barnes. It gnawed at him—smoldering, deep-seated, and rancorous.

In an unprecedented move (politically naïve at best or politically petty at worst) the "Dove" dissension groups declared war on their own—those U.S. military men and women fighting for the freedom of foreigners who were being oppressed and terrorized in their own land. Adam Barnes attributed nobility to those servicemen who participated in any fight-for-freedom venture. He had lost respect for those U.S. countrymen who traveled overseas to protest the war and their own nation's role in it. Such behavior by students and starlets, activists and actors, was being reported as happening in London, Paris, and even Hanoi.

During his internship Barnes used to seethe whenever he tuned in to the nightly news broadcasts. He preferred episodes of Sesame Street which were televised just prior to the evening commentary programs. The humor of Bert and Ernie along with the Duke-blue Cookie Monster had a preemptive calming effect on him as he prepared for the network's bad news of the day emphasis. The contrasts were striking. "Please and thank you" versus "do this, give me that, and you owe me."

What exasperated Adam Barnes most regarding the war was this: after the Tet Offensive, if the U.S. government had handled the situation rightly with soft-spoken diplomacy and a "big stick," he possibly would not be in Vietnam. Instead he would be actively pursuing board certification for pediatrics in some approved residency program. Now he must control his anger, fulfill his duty, and help these courageous American comrades who probably did not want to be there either.

CHAPTER 10

NEW DOCS ON THE LOW BLOCKS

Dodging the raindrops from the various roof eaves and making their way to the mess hall amidst the ascending monsoon mist, Captains Barnes and Jenner found seats with the docs of the 15th Medical Battalion. The food was floating in grease—the same consistency of the sweat oozing from their pores. Thank goodness for T-shirts and a post-storm breeze whiffing across the ridge upon which the dining hall was located.

The conversation among the medical officers revolved mostly around medicine, sports, and the evening movie. There were the usual fraternal questions of, "Where are you from? Where did you do your training? How in the hell did you end up in Vietnam?" Most of the men had specialty medical experience, having evaded the draft to complete their training in general surgery or internal medicine. President Lyndon Johnson's medical call-up of 1968 had gotten them too. Barnes with only a pediatric internship, was probably the least prepared in his field with regard to board certification.

After the meal ended, the troops poured out front where the customary after-dinner basketball game between commissioned officers and enlisted men was being organized. From their observation post on the mess hall porch, Barnes and Jenner, with little persuasion needed, were recruited to fill out the officer team. Their expected role was to be fresh meat for the dominant enlisted hoopsters who had been crushing the command staff every night for weeks.

It was a traditional "shirts and skins" contest—the enlisted participants were stripped to their upper-body skin and the officers were privileged to leave on their sweat-drenched undershirts. The game took place on a single-basket court graded out directly behind a firewall partition separating the MEDEVAC pads from the mess hall. There were no Nike shoes or even "Chuck's" (Chuck Taylor canvas by Converse)—only the breathing mesh boots of the "grunt" and every other ground trooper in the army.

An FYI comment from one of the chopper pilots revealed that the officers had never beaten the more athletic enlisted men since this nightly scheduled "square off" between the rivaling ranks began. Within a few exchanges of defensive prowess on this half-court, mud-wrestling arena, it became clear to the champions that the two new competitors knew how to play. The diversion from the war was exhilarating to all. The game allowed Barnes and Jenner an instant avenue of acceptance into the unit.

Victory was sweet for the officers who had endured such a long-term humiliation at the hand of the lowly enlisted. During the next two weeks a new streak of nightly victories was compiled…the same amount of time it took the CAV to mobilize and move south to III Corps and the Fishhook region along the Cambodian border.

Such a reversal of athletic fortune was not new to Adam Barnes. True competitors thrive on underdog status, especially when pride and the potential to reverse past history and future expectations are at stake.

In 1963, Barnes, a junior undergraduate at Duke University, had the privilege of spending a summer participating in Project: Nicaragua. A mission team comprised of college students was assembled to build a medical clinic on the Atlantic shore of the Central American country. The specific location of the facility was a village community called Pearl Lagoon. The only access to the region was by a two hour dugout canoe ride across a wide expanse of inland waterways and lakes. Supplies had been shipped in that spring; and one member of the team was a second-year medical school student, Ben Givens—another West Virginia product. Barnes considered this project an excellent opportunity to test the medical missionary waters as to whether he would like to serve in that capacity some day. Observing Givens for a short time as he calmly and compassionately handled the up-at-dawn, daily long lines of ill villagers provided Barnes with a memorable model for doing mission work.

When the Duke students arrived in Managua, the nation's capital, they spent the first days and nights of orientation in a Baptist *colegio,* whose missionary directors were West Virginia Baptists too. Over dinner the first night, the pastor presented a dare for a duel to the *norteamericanos* on the basketball court. It seemed that the previous project teams had been challenged similarly by the local amateur basketball team of young adults, two of which had played for the Nicaraguan National Team in the 1960 Olympics. This team had so soundly defeated the U.S. students last summer at their own game, a first for the little Latin

American country, that the jubilation of victory would be compared to storming the court after an ACC basketball rivalry game when the underdog home team has just pulled off the upset of a nationally ranked opponent. The Latin players were excited about the possibility of making it two wins in a row!

This year only one other Duke student had any basketball experience other than Barnes. He was a PK of a divinity school professor at Yale and his experience was in high school and intramural play. The hastily organized match was scheduled for an outdoor "arena" in the center of Managua on the following day.

The results of this international contest were similar to those between the AIR CAV enlisted men and the officer corps that first night at An Khe. Adam Barnes registered his highest point total in a timed and officiated basketball game. He swished the nets for over fifty points, leading the Duke contingent to an easy victory and restoring honor to United States basketball. It did not hurt that at six foot three, Barnes was the tallest player on the court.

The morning haze was rising like a dissipating fog as the CAV pulled out of the Corps headquarters en route to their new field of operations. The III Corps tactical zone covered a region north of Saigon spreading northwest to the Cambodian frontier. The western side of the boundary was sparsely inhabited by Cambodians but heavily populated by North Vietnamese regulars according to intelligence reports. NVA troop concentrations there amounted to three full divisions at last count.

Transport south turned out to be much more comfortable than the stressful, physically fatiguing traveling game of helicopter hopscotch that had brought Captain Barnes all the way to the DMZ. Just a Chinook and a C-130 ride and 15th MED was deposited in Phuoc Vinh, the battalion's new headquarters.

Barnes still had not been assigned to his permanent duty station. It would be another week before he would receive orders to become the battalion surgeon of 1st Battalion 30th Artillery. Battalion surgeon was the title for any general medical officer who oversaw unit medical care. It was not a reference to being certified in any specialty of surgery. Brian Jenner, trained as a dentist, was transferred to the rear at Long Binh where he was aligned with a clinic attached to the Admin company of the AIR CAV. The two friends would not cross paths again for over eight months.

The new mission for the First Air Cavalry Division was two-fold: to create a secure area encompassing all the regional towns and villages of III Corps by means of a surge of force and secondly, to interdict the enemy supply lines routed out of Cambodia. This region had been overwhelmed by terrorism toward innocent civilians. Undermining the economy of the small villages was the heavy Viet Cong taxation. Guerrillas would coerce the collections out of the limited resources of these poor peasants. Only the children seemed bold enough to share such information with Barnes' interpreter. Rarely would any adult speak beyond medical concerns. They seemed too terrified of the consequences.

Though pacification was the goal, the primary problem clearly was the absence of security. The locals were terrorized, regularly experiencing brutality, mental and physical, at the hands of the Communist insurgents. Leaders would have their throats slit, women and children would be threatened with bodily harm, and religious priests would be killed for any opposition to the rebellion.

In the long history of Indochina conflicts, provincial civil service personnel were kidnapped and killed by the thousands according to unverified reports. Under such circumstances the desire for freedom can easily be choked by the tyranny of terrorization. Those who live free and have never experienced such fear firsthand, find it hard to appreciate the incapacitating pressure that was associated with the threat of violence. Barnes, at first, saw this endemic fearfulness as weakness until he was exposed to how powerful a force terrorism can be. For the indigenous inhabitants, to resist the overbearing bullies meant almost certain retaliation upon their families, their physical well-being, and could cost them their lives.

CHAPTER 11

CALL TO CANNONS
IN THE CAVALRY

Lieutenant Colonel (LTC) George Guthrie oversaw the mission of 15th Medical Battalion as its ranking officer in command. This career soldier, educated at Medical College of Virginia in Richmond, had been trained at Walter Reed in internal medicine. He had risen up the ranks in Washington, D.C. with only one previous hardship tour of duty in South Korea, a culture quite foreign to his hometown of Trenton, New Jersey. Guthrie was a heavyset man, most affable in personality and presentation. Though he was soft-spoken, his facial expressions could communicate a sternness without a spoken word. His tone was neutral but firm.

LTC Guthrie had sent for Captain Barnes to discuss a promised on-the-job training (OJT) position in pediatric medicine while serving in Vietnam. Barnes had just completed his internship. Many Army physicians had been promised OJT in their specialties, "if available." The colonel was sensitive to such situations. Since no opportunities existed at the moment in pediatrics, Guthrie had assigned Barnes to a support artillery group with the First Air Cavalry Division. (Interestingly, Stonewall Jackson's first commission after graduating from West Point was as a lieutenant in the army artillery, completing a meritorious tour in that command role during the 1846-48 Mexican War.)

This was the commander's reasoning behind Adam's assignment: the 1st/30th Battalion's general medical officer was nearing his DEROS day. Imbedded with the artillery unit for six months now, this particular doctor had begun to do some Medical Civic Action Program (MEDCAP) work in the area villages. Most of the patients he treated turned out to be children. Based on these MEDCAP clinics, Colonel Guthrie felt that an opportunity for pediatric practice would be a good match for Barnes in the interim. Barnes agreed.

The 1st/30th currently had gun batteries at nine LZs of the AIR CAV from Phuoc Vinh headquarters base to Loc Ninh firebase near the Cambodian border. Obviously this would mean a lot of flight time for Captain Barnes, which did not thrill him. However, he was learning to tolerate the lessened turbulence of the helicopter ride. The stomach stayed where it was designed to stay—in the abdominal cavity, not up in his throat.

At each of these firebases a minimum of two 155mm howitzer gun emplacements would exist. In most cases one field medic would be assigned to care for the health concerns of the LZ battery. These artillery docs were under the supervisory command of the battalion surgeon. Contact with the medics was maintained by radio and regular rounds on the ground. The First Cav would be extremely efficient at getting Barnes around to the various LZs—out and back usually by light observation helicopters (LOHs). Rank had its privileges and being an officer and a physician had even greater advantages, especially when scheduling travel. Making "house calls" via helicopter, like the MEDCAP operations, became another diversion in the midst of war.

Captain Barnes was blessed with some outstanding field medics. These men who would respond to the cry of "medic" instantly during the height of battle were most deserving of respect. And in the CAV, they got it. Even when Barnes cautioned them strongly to wait till there was a lull in the fighting before putting their own lives in danger, they still were stat to risk personal harm to save a fallen friend. All nine of Barnes' medics earned the Combat Medic's Badge for their service in the field. That served as a medal of honor for the courageous work they and all army medics did.

Included in this group of nine field medics were two conscientious objectors (COs). Chaplains and medics were accorded the option of carrying a weapon or not—the only two army groups given that choice. Both of Barnes' CO medics carried no weapons and were admired and highly regarded by the unit soldiers with whom they served. Ironically though, only one of these two left Vietnam on DEROS day as a man whose conscience still prevented him from taking up arms in the midst of battle.

The conversion to active combatant John Evans, a draftee who was assigned to medical corps because of his CO status, happened at LZ Grant. Reared in Utah, Evans had only been in country one month when his company support base came under attack from out of Cambodia. It was near dawn. The enemy had launched a strike on the western perimeter of the camp. During the prelude of mortar fire, several soldiers were wounded. Subsequently, "Charlie" was attempting to cut through the inner ring of concertina wire surrounding the CAV firebase. While Evans was tending an injured gunner in the pit, an NVA regular charged over the embankment and entered the gun well. Instinctively the medic picked up his buddy's weapon and returned fire to drive the enemy back over the mound of dirt. A constant stream of bullets landing all around his body had triggered a defensive response which overrode his human conscience. He survived and was never again without a weapon for the remainder of his year in country.

The second medic who was aligned with the Nui Ba Dinh batteries of the 1st/30th remained true to his CO beliefs: no weapons. Both men served gallantly and effectively for the full extent of their combat tours.

It was Barnes' experiential contention that every combat medic with whom he served provided unheralded care for their comrades in arms, insuring that the first stage of medical care was carried out with skill and that the MEDEVAC process went well. Survival and recovery for a wounded warrior depended upon the dedication of these young medical men-at-arms (or in some cases without arms).

One of Barnes' favorite firebases was up on the aforementioned Nui Ba Dinh, a bump of a mountain which seemed to have erupted right up through the jungle floor. All that could be seen for miles across the flat landscape was this rise in the earth's surface and a twin hump of elevation to the east called Nui Ba Ra. From the vantage peak of Dinh, Barnes could observe the war being waged across the lower plain. Air strikes and bombing runs by the U.S. Air Force could be viewed in full panorama at eye level. Most spectacular were the nighttime attacks by "Puff, the Magic Dragon," a refitted C-130 aircraft capable of dropping a 360-degree curtain of deadly ordnance. Tracer bullets would illuminate the sky spraying down like fireflies in a row to impact one-by-one on the concentric rings of a target. "What could survive such a fire from heaven?" was the logical question in Barnes' mind. Amazingly, the answer to the question was the enemy! Apparently with the depth of the tunnel complexes engineered by the Viet Cong, humankind could survive the surface onslaught and rise to fight again.

On the north slope of Nui Ba Dinh, sprawling up from the foothills was a Montagnard village. The mountaineer people of the region were peasants, rural outcasts who had been ignored over the ages by the ruling families of the populated regions of Indochina. The clans of the Central Highlands of South Vietnam preferred to be left alone to carry on their ancient agrarian customs without interference from national governing bodies or foreign forces of any kind. Their ancestors had lived free and independent, and so, they believed, should they. Unfortunately some of the more harsh oppression from the communist insurgents seemed to be aimed at these innocent tribal folk.

During the French colonial days, a small orphanage had been erected in this village. More recently in the early sixties, the Christian Children's Foundation had taken over its administration. Supported by this worldwide missionary group the orphanage housed about two dozen children ranging in age from two to ten. As a humanitarian endeavor, this charitable compound was viewed by all sides as a neutral, no-fire zone. These children were to be left out of the war—and astonishingly, they were.

The orphanage had a French name, *"Le Berger Del Colline,"* which translated meant "Shepherd of the Hill." The children's home was staffed by missionary nurses under the supervision of

a Montagnard pastor, Nguyen Thuy. These selfless compassionate Christians feared only God. Their war was against hunger,
malnutrition, infectious disease, and anything that threatened
their cherubic charges, most of whom were victims of the war
having lost their parents in some tragedy of hostility. As sole sur-
vivors, each simple soul had been brought to a haven of refuge
on the mountain. Here they would experience the human rights
of life, liberty, and love: the rights that were under assault in the
hamlets across the jungle plateaus, beyond the foothills of these
two mountain blips on the radar.

Every time that Barnes landed for a visit on Nui Ba Dinh, he
made a point to venture down from the firebase to drop in to
the orphanage. If he could help this mission in any way, that was
where his heart was. He readily offered supplies or consultations
at just the hint of a need.

Back in Phuoc Vinh the regular routines of battalion surgeon
for Barnes were becoming entrenched habits after one month.
Then out of the blue an OJT opportunity in Saigon was offered.
It was a chance to go to the rear and study pediatric infectious
disease in Vietnam. An adjunct to this new assignment would be
a pilot project to implement pediatric preventive care as a part of
the pacification program.

Colonel Guthrie came to the aid station of Captain Barnes to
offer this change of venue. It would be a choice that Adam Barnes
would be permitted to make, though this was quite unusual for
the Army, a command-oriented organization. In the conversation Colonel Guthrie noted that Doctor Barnes had made a

strong impression on the 1st/30th officers and enlisted men over the time he was with the unit. Barnes' willingness to fly out and spend nights at the various firebases was greatly appreciated since this was not the usual practice. Guthrie acknowledged that the request from 1st/30th Artillery to keep Barnes could override his thinking if Barnes agreed to stay.

Adam was in a quandary. Colonel Guthrie was in a hurry. He was not giving the Captain much time to ponder his resurgent dilemma. This was the reverse of "hurry up and wait." The whole OJT thing had been one of "wait…and now hurry up." Such was the perplexity of army life.

At hand was a second, unsolicited opportunity to be relocated honorably out of harm's way back to a safer environment. To work in a laboratory setting in the rear, for what more could one ask? What fool would refuse that choice in a war zone? For Barnes, the battle was not an external debate. In his heart emotional criteria were competing and complicating the decision: "Would this be like quitting the field? Would this be viewed as cowardice in his own conscience? Or would this just be the making of a wise choice with positive secondary consequences?"

After what seemed like an eternity in stillness, Barnes prayed silently, "Lord, please help me make the right decision…T I B I A." (TIBIA was his shorthand acronym for "Thanks I Bring In Advance." Just like "tibia," the name of the bone in the lower leg.)

At the completion of this prayer Barnes heard himself utter these words to the colonel: "Sir, I've always played on the first team. If it's all the same to you, I'll stay with the First Team."

With eye-to-eye contact, Guthrie challenged, "You sure?"

Barnes' response was an immediate, "Yes, Sir!" along with the obligatory salute.

That was the end of it. As hokey as his response might have sounded, Captain Adam Barnes would remain permanently assigned to the First Air Cavalry Division, 15th Medical Battalion. No doubts, no regrets…yet always with Satan's surge of second guessing—"You fool!"—then it was done.

CHAPTER 12

A FLIRTATION WITH INSUBORDINATION

In the early days of the First Cavs' mission to III Corps, storm showers of rockets and mortar rounds regularly poured torrents of ordnance on the headquarter town of Phuoc Vinh. Launched by the local Viet Cong, these attacks replaced the NVA missile monsoons in the northern sector. In one particular attack the explosive draft of debris came dangerously close to Barnes.

The close call occurred the first night he slept in the officer's barracks at 1st/30th Battalion. Because of the threat of malaria, bed nets were the order of the day—and night. Off in the distance the telltale thumps or pops of fired lofting rounds could be distinguished just before dawn. Captain Barnes was in a deep sleep oblivious to these warning sounds when the *whomp, whomp, whomp* noise began. Startled to consciousness, he pivoted off his cot to run; where to was never considered. As he whirled to go, the bed's net encasement grabbed him like a boa constrictor wrapping around his ankle. Instantly he went down, face first. The tackle executed by the net was a textbook shoestring takedown common for a football field. A whizzing sound whispered past his head. No one else in the room of veterans had moved. The barrage ended almost as soon as it began. A damage assessment could wait till first light since no one was hurt.

Adorning the hooch wall just behind the bar was a poster of Raquel Welch. The beauty was posed, scantily attired in that famous fur-lined bikini. Most of her skin, including her midriff, was exposed. That day, upon closer examination of the poster, the absence of her belly button was noticed. Officers confirmed its presence on the previous evening's perusals. The next morning, it was missing—gone. In its place was a finger-sized hole that cut clear through to the wall. An errant piece of shrapnel (that audible whine) had traversed the room encountering Raquel. "Better she (the poster), than I," thought Barnes. Had he not been wrestled to the floor by his mosquito net, Barnes, too, could have been a punctured portrait, but with more than cosmetic consequences.

These assaults on the base camp of the First Team were primarily a nuisance. On more than one occasion Barnes was caught taking a shower in the makeshift bathing stall when the mortar shower came down. Nothing was more humiliating than to be naked, all covered with soap suds, and forced to dive into a muddy ditch for safety. Nude streaking was associated with peace rallies in the real world; in Vietnam, streaking could be a survival technique in the middle of a war.

"*Gastrocnemius*," snarled Barnes causing a spurt of spit. (Gastrocnemius was Barnes' favorite cuss word equivalent for "*damn*." It could be uttered with such guttural gusto that the innocuous name of a muscle in the leg would explode as an emphatic expletive. Only in the mind and from the mouth of Adam Barnes did it become a powerfully profane pronouncement.) Upon these occasional naked splash downs in the mud, it was his only retort to this enemy-imposed indignity.

In Phuoc Vinh the "walking" of mortar rounds across the air strip could come at any time. The tension level increased exponentially as each exploding round walked closer and closer to an individual body. Response time was critical. "Down on the ground! Quickly! Now!" A soldier had to learn this reflex reaction. If you hear the sound, then you're still alive.

Troops in the rear had to contend with indirect fire attacks from the enemy regularly at first. For this reason, Captain Barnes had instructed his medical staff and tech specialists to elevate the protecting wall of sandbags around the aid station, especially beside their living quarters located in the back. After the Raquel incident, the officers of 1st/30th had already created individual sandbag bunker caves over their beds inside the officer quarters. Seven igloo-shaped structures fit in the hut comfortably, sandbag blocks replacing the traditional snow-packed ones to fashion the domes.

Shortly after erecting the vertical sandbag extension of the aid station bulwark, a conflict arose between command and medical. Since a lack of external symmetry now existed across the camp, headquarters ordered the additions be reduced to the level of the screens on every building in the compound. Though low, the lines must be the same. From Barnes' perspective, this lowering of the bag barriers would not protect the standing or sitting personnel inside these structures. Only those who happened to be in a prone position when the attack started would be shielded from the shelling.

Upon arriving at the aid station for morning sick call, Barnes observed the change. His staff sergeant informed him that the order had come down from the new Exec (executive officer, rank of major). The additional sandbags must be removed.

"Gastrocnemius!"

The screen door burst open with one angry, fisted thrust as Barnes bolted from the aid station without touching a step. In less time than it takes to run a 40-yard dash, he was in the exec's office.

Major Timothy Jones was regular army, somewhere in his midthirties. Barnes and Jones were about the same height, but Jones was stockier. He had only recently been transferred to this artillery battalion.

"Sir, what's with the command to drop the security sandbags from around *my men?*" Barnes asked.

"We have an IG (Inspector General) inspection coming and we need a symmetrical look on the outside of all our buildings," was Jones' answer.

"But, Sir," Barnes replied, stifling his rage, "I am concerned about the safety of my medics. Being in the aid station makes them more vulnerable to rocket and mortar attacks than in the other billets."

"Captain Barnes, the normal level of sandbags is more than adequate."

Exhibiting his trait of being a bit more outspoken when he was angry, Barnes kept on.

"It's not safe, sir. The aid station sits…"

"Captain," Jones interrupted with an exasperated tone, "we failed our last IG inspection!" He punctuated his point with a forceful gesture as he turned from a filing cabinet. Clutched in his hand was the rolled up IG report. "It won't happen again on my watch."

"Yes, sir!" As Barnes bounded out the door without touching the steps, his mind was mulling over the thought that the safety of men should always take precedence over any piddling IG inspection.

Because of an uptick in the priorities of the war, the IG inspection was postponed the very next week.

Captain Adam Barnes was not reared to challenge authority intentionally. It just seemed to happen naturally. However, circumstances tended to dictate Barnes' bold defiance in the military. Poor distribution of simple medical supplies out to the field was such a circumstance. He followed the normal channel for requisitioning bug repellent, anti-fungal ointment, steroid cream, bandages, and even sandbags. After waiting for weeks and sometimes months for the supplies, Barnes took matters into his own hands. His plan was to assign Private First Class Bobby Johnson to a liaison position in the 93rd Evacuation Hospital at Long Binh. That just so happened to be First Cav's rear supply depot. On the surface, Private Johnson was to provide follow-up information on evacuated soldiers, coordinating their medical care process through the clinical chaos of an evacuation hospital. Beneath the surface, Bobby Johnson was a first-class scrounger, a hunter of previously requisitioned items that were clogged in logistical purgatory. From his location at Long Binh he developed a friendship with the CAV depot sergeant. (Bobby could scratch the backs or charm the socks off anybody. His personal motivation was to stay in the rear in order to avoid returning to the field; for that reason he became a most successful forager.)

Eventually, because of this friendly relationship, the rear supply sergeant gave 1st/30th requisitions some preferential treatment in the shipping schedules. Needed medical supplies soon were procured and transferred in a more expeditious manner. The system was working well—or so it seemed.

One day Colonel Guthrie dropped by the aid station in Phuoc Vinh unexpectedly for a visit. Taking Barnes outside, he inquired if he knew a Private Bobby Johnson, on temporary duty in Long Binh. Barnes acknowledged that he did. The colonel then asked if Barnes was aware of what Private Johnson had been doing there. Barnes again acknowledged that he did without confirming any of the specific details.

Colonel Guthrie's response was succinct. "Stop it!" As he turned to go, he looked back and made direct eye contact with Barnes. "Don't do it again!"

The colonel was well aware of the division-wide supply problem, but he knew that meeting the need in such an unorthodox way could create a problem if every general medical officer circumvented the standard operating procedures of the requisitioning system—no matter how poorly the process was functioning.

George Guthrie was a good man. He was also near DEROS.

CHAPTER 13

MEDCAP

How does one win the battle for hearts and minds among the oppressed? By showing that the purported "oppressors" are not oppressing. In the rural regions of South Vietnam the two competing strategies were propaganda versus pacification—on one side, Communist propaganda reinforced by terrorism; on the other, peace by security. The lines between the two did get blurred at times from some overlapping, especially in the more urban areas. Yet, out in the paddies, jungles, and hills, hopeful signs were noticeable. Roads that needed repair were being repaired, both for vehicular transportation and personal communication.

In III Corps, the U.S. Army was accelerating its participation in the MEDCAP program. Such an outing was a welcomed change of pace from the fighting war. Since the majority of the patients were of pediatric age—an interesting reality—Adam Barnes felt right at home. He found true joy in helping a sick child to become well. He was always haunted by the thought that a doctor may have been able to save the life of his baby brother, Dana. Barnes was now driven to be that doctor for someone else's brother, no matter what nationality, race, or religion.

The captain's initial exposure to MEDCAP came within his first week with 1st/30th Battalion in Phuoc Vinh. The common practice was for a company of CAV infantrymen to cordon off a U.S. Command-designated village in the vicinity. These grunts, as they called themselves, would set up a safe perimeter around the town in the early morning. Then around ten o'clock the medical contingent would arrive to conduct a spontaneous and brief outpatient clinic. These sick calls usually lasted no more than two hours for the sake of security. The suddenness of the operation and the lack of a set routine served to keep the enemy off balance and denied the opportunity to disrupt the event. No set or recurrent patterns of schedule or locale could be attempted because *the enemy was most efficient at detecting timing tendencies and habitual behavior.* One minute a doctor was in the marketplace or a village churchyard seeing patients referred by word of mouth; the next minute he was gone. Not a good way to practice medicine, but an effective way to get positive exposure in the homes and hamlets.

Then there were the children. The playful exuberance displayed by the various village innocents tended to mask the actuality of a war zone. On these sporadic outings, Adam often reflected on the reality that he was getting to fulfill the very dream of his friend, Claire Marshall—that of being a "medical mother" on an overseas mission. How special was the experience to minister to a forsaken (or at least it seemed so) segment of God's family, the cherub-like little ones of light. Barnes imagined that maybe after the war an opportunity would present itself for him to share his pediatric adventures with "Clairee."

Surprisingly to Adam, with his mental musings about his nurse friend came unexpected twinges of pain, a heartache, a renewed stabbing of anguish. These emotional surges seemed to be triggered by remembering Claire: her smile, her gloriously long flowing hair, her distinct features of natural form and facial beauty. Yet any feelings of tenderness for her had been scarred over, still taboo to be acknowledged. She was an *engaged woman*. For now, his recollections must be relegated to fantasies flashing like a jet across the fabric of his mind's sky—high above his emotional reservoir—images suddenly visible, then vanquished from view.

In the Phuoc Vinh region the children were the most trusting. They popped up like ants drawn to sugar before the equipment and pharmaceutical boxes could even be arranged for disposition. Underlying the process was the hope that the Vietnamese adults might learn from the children that an American medical doctor had come into the area, in the square, or at the storefront. An ailing adult might risk the local consequences of the Cong to seek help. In reality, the truly sick of the village rarely made it to the clinic in the two hours provided. Many who could have been treated never got there in time to be seen.

Assigned to Barnes for these hamlet house-calls was Sergeant Tam, an Army of the Republic of Vietnam (ARVN) interpreter. His role in the MEDCAP clinic was to listen to the patient, investigate the chief complaint, and clarify it for the doctor. The chain of communication was crucial since there were no lab facilities. Physical diagnosis was the name of the game. A missed diagnosis could hinge on a single word in the patient's history or the review of systems. All Barnes knew of the language at this point was *con dau* (pain) to use with the question, "Where does it hurt?" Barnes was the *dai uy* (captain) and the *bac si* (doctor), but Tam was the practitioner of the art. Like any gifted nurse, he made the doctor look good. It started with Tam translating the symptoms and ended with Tam explaining the treatment and detailing how the prescribed medicine was to be taken.

Sergeant Tam had no medical training prior to this assignment. He was drafted just like Barnes, with one striking difference. Barnes was in the army for *two years;* Tam, for an *eternity.* That truth was troubling to the Vietnamese sergeant, though he hid it well.

Tam grew up near Saigon. He spoke fluent French and more than adequate English, though his medical vernacular was a work in progress. He was young at age twenty-four, but seemed older. He and his wife of six years had an apartment in Saigon. They had a two-year-old daughter. The in-laws looked after the family while Sergeant Tam served in the field. He would get back home possibly twice a year.

Though his primary task was not to be an interpreter for the medical team, it was obvious that he genuinely sought the camaraderie of the aid station. An understanding of medicine and its practice provided both pleasure and power to him. He absorbed knowledge like a sponge dipped in this new watering pool of the healing lore. In Vietnamese society medical knowledge meant prestige; perhaps for Tam this would be a vocational choice when the war was over.

On another day just outside of Phuoc Vinh, the MEDCAP team's vehicles turned off the rutted roadway onto the village green. The local priest intercepted the lead jeep in front of his church. Tam inquired about any sickness in the village. The young man in simple vestments that designated his calling seemed nervous and uncomfortable, qualities uncommon to the clergy it seemed to Barnes. Tam brought the priest over to the captain and revealed why the man appeared apprehensive.

Yes, there were sick people in the community but they were in the hut of those whom the priest suspected as being Viet Cong sympathizers. He adamantly encouraged the team to avoid that particular hut. It would be too risky to offer care to them. The decision, however, was left to Captain Barnes.

At this early point in his tour of duty, still the idealist as a healer and unsophisticated as a soldier of war, Barnes decided to enter the hut with Tam. The priest stayed back 100 feet away in the churchyard.

Inside the shadowy enclosure sectioned with bamboo partitions were four people: a *mama-san* (mother) and three men. Clearly, they were incapacitated with illness. Soon it was confirmed that the men were quite feverish. A preliminary diagnosis of malaria was made. The older man had the yellow eyeballs and his skin was markedly jaundiced. Upon physical examination he was noted to have an extremely enlarged liver and spleen. The younger two only had palpably large spleens which is why Barnes attributed their condition to an acute attack of malaria. Tam was able to elicit a history of severe chills and sweats. All three men were evacuated to a Vietnamese hospital for treatment in spite of the cautionary claim from the priest that these men were Viet Cong. At the end of the day, Barnes was just excited about seeing some serious pathology diseases (malaria and hepatitis), diagnosing, and referring them. It was just an afterthought that he may have provided comfort and care to the enemy.

Such a simplistic practice of medicine on these MEDCAPs might seem to some to be from the Dark Ages in technique—first aid on the frontier. Yet to go back in time and observe the miracle of what penicillin could do as a wonder drug again was awe-inspiring to Barnes. Children with bacterial infections would respond within twenty-four hours of just one intramuscular (IM) injection. Most of these Asian bacterial cells had never encountered such potent antibiotics on any previous field of battle, a definite advantage if only a temporary one. The Vietnamese children greatly benefited and the young doctor was buoyed up by the leverage he seemed to have against infectious disease.

In children, behavioral and cultural similarities seemed to exist worldwide—parallels in playful antics and facial mannerisms were exhibited by the Vietnamese children, the same as Barnes had observed in the kids of West Virginia. The Asian kids were curious about anything and inquisitive about everything. Strangers in the village brought excitement to their humdrum daylight hours.

Captain Barnes had requested and received periodic care packages of candy from family and church groups stateside. However, only one out of every three boxes made it through to the field. As rewards, the medics would distribute the candy to the pediatric patients being treated. Whatever was left over on a given day would be doled out to the children bystanders, usually a sizable crowd.

A humorous moment could arise just because these were kids. One incident was particularly memorable to Barnes. A little four-year-old boy had arrived on the scene too late and had missed out on the candy handouts. In leaving, the jeep in which Barnes was riding pulled across an open field dissecting it as a shortcut exit from the hamlet. The little tyke was walking away on a similar path. His head and shoulders were drooping; a more dejected child the doc had never seen. Adam's heart went out to him. The kid was shirtless and shoeless; wearing what appeared to be GI boxer shorts, which hung down below his knees. Such a sad sight.

At the very instant when the army jeep passed the child walking alone, Barnes glimpsed an overlooked small bag of miniature candy bars stashed in the backseat. Either it had fallen out of the treat box inadvertently or it was being saved intentionally for another time. It did not matter to Barnes. He held it up so the child could identify what it was and then tossed it like a bean bag so it landed five yards ahead of the boy. The jeep moved on.

The look of amazement, then grateful anticipation on the child's face was etched in the mind of Captain Barnes. A treasure had been thrown at the feet of this diminutive lad. Just a step away was a goldmine of goodies all for him.

As the boy lurched after the "spoils of war," his underwear slipped from his waist and the elastic band entangled his ankles. The sudden encumbrance tackled him down. He looked up through the created puff of dust only to see the pack of nearby children swooping in and carrying off his quarry of candy. Recovering from the fall to reclaim just one piece of sweetness was out of the question for this ill-fated toddler.

Turning back to comfort the boy was out of the question too. What was the depth of disappointment for this Vietnamese child? How long would the feeling last? Probably not very long, Barnes thought, as his vehicle intersected the main road back to Phuoc Vinh. Barnes was the blest one. He had been privileged to witness that blissful expression in the child's face when the bag was dropped in his proverbial lap. That mental image was to be conjured up by Barnes every time the care packages were distributed. Could the people of Vietnam receive the gift of freedom that was within their reach? Barnes hoped so.

CHAPTER 14

A PAINLESS PEOPLE

P ain in the Vietnamese culture was a fascination to Adam Barnes, as he compared it with his experience growing up in the United States. Minor aches and pains could elicit tears and tantrums from American children whereas similar responses were rarely present with the Vietnamese. Anecdotal research offered a clue to Barnes: in the Asian family pain seemed not to be reinforced with comforting words and coddling responses. There was no pampering or picking up the child to counter the crying as was done in the States. However, western kids have been classically conditioned that the tear-shedding technique will be rewarded with some self-gratifying result. At all costs, whimpering, whining, weeping, and waling are to be controlled by a consoling word or an endearing caress or an all-embracing hug—actions not necessarily wrong but which have conditioning consequences in a child.

It was only on rare occasions that Barnes had heard crying from a Vietnamese child. On the contrary, the reaction by these young ones to any physical trauma was usually tearless. On one MEDCAP outing, a young boy, shirtless and barefoot, limped through the storefront opening and was hoisted onto a wooden table, cleared for the purpose of physical examination. Not a sound was uttered from the child…or the army medics as they stood by marveling at the silence. The youngster was estimated to be about nine years old. On his right leg bulging three inches across the kneecap was a huge abscess—red, angry-looking, hot, and fluctuant.

Since no xylocaine for numbing was available in the treatment box (a makeshift use of a wooden artillery shell container), Barnes decided to lance the lesion with a bayonet-tip scalpel—without the benefit of local anesthesia. Tam explained word by word to the mother and child what the plan of treatment was. The mother's eyes bulged wide as she stepped back to lean against the bamboo doorjamb. Beneath a fringe of banged hair, the boy's eyes turned up and his mouth turned down, he sat unshrinkingly on the table with his leg dangling over the edge. His demeanor suspicious, but unafraid.

Betadine antiseptic was painted like a bull's-eye around the taut skin of the knee. The boy was instructed to look away. Instead, he chose first to make full eye contact with the doctor, and then returned his gaze back to the knee. With one motion, Barnes drove the blade point into the abscess, sweeping it up swiftly through the tissue in an arc. Pus poured out as the pressure was released. The patient tightened his grip on the adjacent medic's wrist but sat still, motionless, expressing absolutely no visible emotion.

The doctor had anticipated a struggle since a kid back home would have been on the ceiling and through the roof, but this Vietnamese boy barely flinched a muscle. Even when some of the pockets of the abscess were broken down to insure adequate drainage, the child was as stoic as they come. Surely the boy had known pain in his short life, but apparently he had been conditioned to "walk it off." With time, drainage, packing, bandaging, and penicillin another miracle of the art of medicine would take place.

Not all of the practice of field medicine was painless. Even penicillin can cause pain. Over the months Tam served as the MEDCAP interpreter, he became a very good diagnostician and practitioner of first aid. However, not all of his techniques were appropriate for the situation in which he applied them.

On one unusually busy sick-call day, an ARVN corporal came by with a severely infected index finger on his left hand. He first went to Tam for help, and Tam came inside the aid station for consultation with Barnes. The doctor stepped outside briefly to confirm the inflammatory signs that Tam had described. Barnes concurred that a shot of penicillin would work wonders and instructed Tam to administer it. Tam left to carry out the injection.

Suddenly, howls of utter agony came from the courtyard. Barnes stopped examining his patient and rose up to check the source of the ear-piercing eruption. There stood Tam laboring at one end of a hypodermic syringe. At the other end, the ARVN soldier. Tam had inserted the tip of the needle into the infected finger, the web of the hand being the skin-piercing point. Tam was attempting to squeeze the thick penicillin emulsion into the narrow joint space of the finger rather than injecting the IM drug into the corporal's buttocks. A re-insertion into the correct anatomy and all was well within twenty-four hours.

Since security was a constant concern for each MEDCAP event, overtime was not an option. The "game" was played on a very strict timeline. That reality would always be troubling to a conscientious doctor with sick patients still in the waiting room. Such was the case in the village of Phuoc Hua I.

As the two-hour clinic was fast coming to a close, a mother with a six-month-old baby appeared in the market square. She approached the staff and placed her infant on the wooden examining table. He lay quite stiff on the covering blanket. He was burning up with fever. His eyes were sunken while the fontanel openings of his developing skull were bulging. The rigidity in his neck was a serious sign. The young mother was informed that the baby needed to go to a hospital to be treated for dehydration and tested for meningitis. Tam interpreted the situation in simple but compelling terms: she and the baby should be transported in the doctor's jeep immediately.

The mother seemed hesitant and told the interpreter that she needed to go home first to get a few things. The urgency was explained again but she insisted that she would be right back with the baby.

The Vietnamese woman had not been gone from the market square for more than two minutes when explosions and gunfire began to occur on the perimeter of the village. Simultaneously the CAV company commander barreled into the town with two other personnel carriers filled with grunts.

"Why are you in Phuoc Hua II?" he barked. "We set up your security in Phuoc Hua I! All hell is breaking loose out there. You've got to leave now. We'll cover you!"

The chaos of combat precluded any delay to pick up the mother and her sick baby. Withdrawal was immediate to Barnes' great dismay. He pondered whether the infant could survive another day without care. He agonized over all the possible outcomes, reassuring himself with the axiom that "God made babies tough!"

Adam Barnes did not sleep well that night. He knew the impact on a family of the death of an infant. His brother, Dana, had been the same age when he died.

———————————

The answer to the life or death question arrived near noon the next day. Specialist Vic Allen, the aid station's med tech, entered the examining bay cradling the limp body of a baby. An emotionally distraught Vietnamese woman was being restrained at the door. She was inconsolable. Barnes recognized the mother from the previous day's madcap MEDCAP. His heart sank to the pit of his stomach. Specialist Allen frantically began to set up for resuscitation.

Barnes knew what a dead infant looked like. He had seen his brother Dana at death. He had been only five when he took that peek through the baby bed railing and came face-to-face with *death*. Initially the aid station staff had wanted to start CPR but Barnes knew it was too late.

"He's dead."

"How do you know?"

"I know."

All the signs were there: no carotid pulse in the neck, pupils fixed and dilated, bluish skin color, no breath sounds.

Barnes grabbed an ophthalmoscope to make a quick check of the retinal eye grounds. He knew what he would find. He hoped he would be wrong. "Lord, please help us." "Boxcars" lined the vascular tracks of the retina confirming that the child was long dead. No hope, only heaven for this littlest of angels.

A cursory exam of the baby's body revealed a chronology of failed care. Upon his back were the telltale bruises of Chinese medicine utilized by some practitioner last evening. When the child worsened, the mother had taken the infant to the local Vietnamese doctor with whom Barnes had worked. Now the circuitous referral had returned to Barnes, only too late.

What haunted Adam Barnes was the belief that this child would have been saved. If the mother had only left with them the day before. If she had brought the child directly to the American gate for care instead of going to the village Chinese doctor. If she had bypassed the Vietnamese physician and come straight to the aid station, the child could have been saved. Those precious hours may have made all the difference. Another miracle missed.

Where do you direct your anger when the innocent die needlessly? At the situation? At man? At God? Barnes had not unraveled the reason for his episodic feelings of rage. All he knew now was that he was resentfully angry. He had yet to ascertain with any tranquil satisfaction a rationale for senseless suffering in the world, especially that afflicted upon mere children through no fault of their own.

CHAPTER 15

ASSAULT OF THE KILLER BEES

As a battalion surgeon, Adam Barnes was based the farthest out in the army chain of care that a medical doctor would be positioned in the field. In spite of the title designation of surgeon, when the knife fell at eight in the morning, one would not expect to find a pediatric intern in the operating room with a scalpel. Even if a chance to cut could mean a chance to cure, that would be a job for a certified surgeon, not a general medical officer. In fact, based on actual operating room (OR) experience, some of Barnes' older medics had spent more hours in operating suites than he had. Acknowledging their skill and competence, Barnes held his staff of medics with the highest regard. He would put his men up against anyone's. An early encounter with evacuation hospital personnel caused Barnes to recognize the difference between the glorified medic in name and the unheralded medic in action.

A 1st/30th Battalion artilleryman had been evacuated to Long Binh. Barnes had been out making rounds at several landing zone batteries and was following up on his patient at the 93rd Evac. He traveled in full battle gear whenever he went out to visit any firebase: flak jacket, helmet, M16 rifle. As Barnes, covered with a layer of dust from the red clay, stepped out of the helicopter upon landing at the MEDEVAC pad, several army medical personnel were passing by in swimsuits returning from the outdoor swimming pool. Barnes overheard them remark, "Heh, there's a war-doc from the field! Let's get a picture of him with the chopper." Cameras clicked.

"War-doc? From the field?" thought Barnes. "They have no idea."

What a contrast Adam felt between himself and the grunt medic who faced combat almost daily humping through the boonies. Thirty-day stints without bathing facilities...no hot food, no bed and no swimming pool, unless a rain-filled bomb crater counted as an equivalent. Barnes was embarrassed to have been elevated to the status of a combat medic. Those men were out in the field ministering to the 20 percent of American servicemen in Vietnam actually fighting the war.

Battalion surgeons were considered VIPs by the U.S. Army and by the enemy. The death of a physician or a medic translated into the death of all the military personnel these men of medicine could have saved. Docs were targeted because they were very important people in the healing chain of survival.

However, on numerous occasions when a simple, physical labor task needed to be performed at or around the clinic, Barnes disdained over the delay associated with the staff sergeant coordinating a "detail" to carry out the same work "down the road." Therefore, it was not uncommon to find the captain, stripped down to his T-shirt, all insignia of rank removed for security reasons, out on the compound grounds digging a latrine or repairing a building. It was so much easier and by far quicker to do the job himself rather than "hurry up and wait" on the assignment to be done later. Rank did have its privileges, but expedited time was more important to Barnes, especially if he felt his staff had more urgent grunts and grinds than to stop and pursue the trivial.

———————

Yes, from day one the First Cav took great care of their officers. The most secure accommodations, the best rations, and priority transportation to and from any destination were first-class for the First Team physicians. With the exception of the intermittent mortar and rocket attacks, Barnes' face-to-face encounters with the enemy were rare. However there was that one incident with the 1,000 VCBs.

Although many a package from home failed to make it out of the Saigon Depot, one parcel, however, did. It contained a basketball net, a basketball rim, and one flat basketball. Barnes had made the request in correspondence with his family for the recreational articles and they had responded. "Hard Charger" base camp was now complete. (Hard Charger was the historic call name for this artillery unit.) It was a puzzlement why these items were so difficult to get from Special Services in country.

Doctor Barnes fashioned a backboard out of the wood planks of ammo boxes. He nailed the board and rim to a telephone pole. The ten-foot goal was located just adjacent to the mess hall (similar to the setting at An Khe). The games on this half court did not have the tradition of the officer versus enlisted competitions on the DMZ, but casual minutes of diversion did take place from time to time there in the south. However, many a pick-up game would be interrupted by the call to arms. Another round of indirect fire being called in on an enemy position. Launching 155mm rounds from these big artillery cannons in support of troops always took precedent over troops launching balls at basket rims.

One dusty, dry day around mid-morning, it was discovered that a battalion of VC bees (or wasps), led by their Amazon warrior queen had slipped in and taken the high ground for a sniper's nest. The hive was poorly camouflaged in the interwoven infrastructure of the basketball goal net.

A code alert came to Captain Barnes in the aid station. Lunch was about to be served in the company mess hall and the enemy insects had cut off the food supply line at the front. The battalion surgeon took this challenge as a personal affront. Basketball was the national game, invented and refined in the heartland of America. This was the field house of the Hard Chargers and no enemy was going to be permitted to capture home court, especially a squad of VC bees.

A chemical warfare suit—vintage World War II surplus—was stored in the aid station supply closet. It's purpose was to facilitate the administering of medical care in the event of a chemical attack. The outfit looked like a space suit: an enlarged head piece to cover a gas-masked physician and a pair of coveralls effectively sealed at the ankles and waist. Rubber boots and rubber gloves completed the gas gear ensemble.

Quickly, Barnes donned the outfit. He commandeered a water pump fitted with an attachable spray nozzle. The suit and the pump were essential to the washing protocol in decontaminating soldiers who had been exposed to chemicals like tear gas.

Cloaked in the hood like an outer space monster, "Captain Courageous" went forth to battle the deadly VC bees. The drones assailed the bearer of the water weapon with unrelenting suicide strikes as streams of forced fluid immersed the hive continuously.

The integrity of the fortress nest began to falter and the queen commander immediately fell back into the mess hall kitchen to regroup. In one battle, Barnes was victorious as hundreds fell, but the war would go on.

In hot pursuit, in sweaty, hot pursuit, Barnes shuffled his way into the dining facility undaunted to outflank any counterattack. This second surge of the waves of water caused the forming cluster of bees to collapse. Layer by layer they flew off in full retreat to a VC-controlled village to the east—never to mount up as a threat again.

Only a Polaroid snapshot was taken of the mysterious "Captain B." No national network correspondents were present to record the great victory. Only Adam Barnes could bask in the glow of being undefeated…and still champion.

CHAPTER 16

NVA DIVISIONS IN CAMBODIA

From the real war mindset of Adam Barnes, the enemy's Tet Offensive had failed miserably. The American and allied armies had fended off this nationwide long attack with success. When no popular uprising by the South Vietnamese occurred, when the Viet Cong were not welcomed as liberators, and when the insurgent invaders ran out of bullets, only Chieu Hoi (I surrender) remained. For all intents and purposes, the *military* aspect of this war was over. It should have led to a negotiated conclusion there and then. Finished, completed, ended. Unfortunately, it did not. ***It was a war, not a game.***

After the fiery coals of Tet died down and the smoke cleared, the resumption of insurgent tyranny stoked a new flame in an old war. Intimidation tactics had alienated many villagers throughout Vietnam, but fear still was a force. Many pacification projects had been hindered by coercing, kidnapping, and assassinating innocent men, women, and children. The Free World turned a blind eye to this brutality, much as it had during the Holocaust. Media journalism ignored the impact of terrorism in an uncivil war. In the "United" States—a misnomer for sure—the war was called "unjust." Victims of terrorism and tyranny be damned.

After Tet, sanctuaries for the North Vietnamese enemy became an even greater necessity since head to head confrontation had proved futile. Cambodia, despite Prince Sihanouk's oft repeated protestation that his country was neutral, sheltered at least three divisions of the NVA. Intel reports from Long Range Reconnaissance Patrol (LRRP) units and the actual nighttime sightings of convoy truck lights in uninhabited border regions confirmed the presence of NVA regulars no matter what Sihanouk was proclaiming.

Miles of underground pathways tunneled the terrain. The Vietnamese were skilled engineers. Their construction techniques produced a subterranean world, running deep and running long—underground headquarters, hospitals, and housing. West Virginia coal miners would have been impressed with these man-made mazes.

After the military defeat of Tet, the North's strategies turned political and propagandistic. On the other side, the Americans were primarily political in their approach: inflict sufficient suffering on the enemy to force them to negotiate in a favorable fashion with the U.S. and South Vietnamese governments, who were desirous of building a democratic nation, thus avoiding Communist dominion. By comparison, the North Vietnamese also chose to apply pain, but in the form of guerrilla warfare: using trails of tunnels to execute their villainy of injuring and maiming Americans to the point that "their own people will bring them home." The Communist North counted on America to tire of a war of attrition just as had occurred with the citizens of France during the colonial days of Indochina…and as always it would seem, in the middle were innocent people.

Using Eisenhower's imagery of dominoes, Doctor Barnes believed that communism was exerting force on one side of the domino block while the underpinning of the other side was being undermined at the bottom. Depravity and repression on the part of the Saigon government were corrupting the whole stabilizing process. His concern was that American soldiers would be crushed when the wall came toppling down, due to no fault of their own. "All the king's horses and all the king's men" would not be able to restore a wall of freedom for Vietnam.

"Why should American young men die for those who seemed unwilling to fight to free themselves?" Barnes was impassioned about his position that the South Vietnamese people must be willing to make some sacrifices in order to obtain their democratic freedom. It would be no different from what the colonial revolutionaries had done in forming the United States some 200 years before. Those citizens sacrificed their livelihood *and* their lives along with their leaders, strong men of exceptional courage and integrity. The caliber and character of leadership left behind always makes a great difference in the success of a newly freed nation.

The move to Phuoc Vinh was eye-opening for Barnes. The new mission for the CAV was to protect villages and hamlets from direct insurgent attacks. By destroying or driving the enemy away from the area, a new sense of local security could be established—a safer haven which the inhabitants had not known for some time. A transformation of thinking was taking place for the Vietnamese…and for Captain Adam Barnes.

In the first six months that the AIR CAV was in III Corps, a remarkable transition took place. It was palpable and visible—a hopeful beam of light into the darkness. People too terrified to travel in the daytime were now moving about the countryside at night, trusting the Americans for their protection. On the roads and paths timid smiles replaced scornful scowls. Fear was slowly being lessened and in some cases alleviated.

Provincial leaders were stepping up and speaking out to encourage work and commerce. A buffer zone was being built between the bullies and the bullied. What had changed? In a word— security. Roads and villages were more secure, and rocket and mortar launches were pushed farther away. Attacks were reduced with one exception; whenever the currency was exchanged for newly printed bills with totally new designs to prevent hoarding, a "tantrum attack" could be expected the very next night. Such a paper-dollar reissue made all current stashes of money instantly worthless to the locals and money-exchanging profiteers.

As LZ support base locations curved convexly toward Cambodia, conditions in the inner sphere became less perilous; communities were less threatened. The ARVN soldiers were becoming more confident in the province. The Chieu Hoi program of amnesty and rehabilitation was taking hold with increasing defections from the Viet Cong. A taste of peace, a whiff of freedom—was this program succeeding or was it a calm before another storm? Barnes may not have understood all the whys and wherefores, but he did know this: he was developing a whole new perspective on why he was there, why the First Air Cav was there...why the United States military was there.

As the chaplain read a Bible scripture in a Sunday chapel ser-vice, a portion of the passage became etched in Barnes' mind. The context of the verses depicted Jesus of Nazareth in a syna-gogue, as was His Sabbath custom, reading from a scroll of the Prophet Isaiah. After sitting down, Jesus was noted to proclaim to the congregants that He was the fulfillment of the very words He had just uttered...the bold phrase which resonated with Barnes seemed to imply simply that the Messiah had come "to set free those who were oppressed." (Luke 4:18) Until that very moment the doctor had never noticed the possible association between one of Jesus' ministry goals and the American Army's mission objectives. Of course, he kept that kind of thinking to himself. Not very many people would care to acknowledge a con-gruence of purpose for "church and state" that is, freedom for all peoples.

As the preacher droned on with his sermon focus, Adam mentally wandered and wondered what Claire would say about her old friend's enlightenment based on the same passage of scripture. In his daydream, that discussion would have been an interesting one. Vietnam as a mission field of battle for setting oppressed people free. What an irony. But Vietnam was not sup-posed to be a game of semantics. It was a war. Barnes left the worship service fascinated by what was to him a new insight and stimulated by the imagined debate he could carry on with nurse Claire if she were there.

Most of the reports at the evening briefing were routine. The "sitreps" were filled with the usual abbreviations and statistics charted out for easy consumption by the staff and command colonel of 1st/30th Artillery Battalion—MIAs, KIAs WIAs, and various other battle damage assessments (BDAs). Captain Barnes had noted on his briefing chart that an unusual rise in fevers of unknown origin had been detected in the Nui Ba Dinh battery. An outbreak of illness on this mountain top fortress would greatly hinder strategic artillery support in the region. Barnes informed the colonel that he would fly up and examine the whole company for some type of transmissible infection. While he was there, he would also investigate the orphanage adjacent to the firebase to rule it out as a possible source of contagion. Preventive medicine was always the first and foremost priority for the chief medical officer.

The final report of the night was by S-2 Captain Scott Brenskie, a West Point grad from Parma, Ohio. He had a great sense of humor for an intelligence staff officer, but in these presentations he exhibited a self-controlled demeanor speaking in a deep neutral voice like a network newscaster—no emotion, just the facts. That night he seemed to Barnes to be extremely somber as he began to deliver his report.

"In the Fishhook area," he pointed to the operation's map, "there has been an attack on LZ Brass, a 9th Army Division base." He paused for a moment. "An unconventional attack by NVA standards."

Captain Brenskie went on to describe the northern enemy's attempt to overrun this isolated firebase on the Cambodian border. The attackers barely made it through the first row of concertina wire.

The S-2 continued. "And here's the puzzler. These NVA soldiers were just boys fourteen-, fifteen-, and sixteen-year-old kids."

After the briefing that evening, Barnes and Brenskie sat on their beds in the officers' quarters and talked about the firebase attack and how reckless it seemed for NVA strategists. Barnes was shocked upon learning that these boys had only recently been conscripted off the streets of Hanoi. With mere weeks of instruction they had been thrust as pawns upon this outpost with zero chance of success. He strained to grasp a why? What was the strategy? What was the ulterior plan?

Brenskie had an explanation. It was even more bizarre for Barnes to get his mind around. Several North Vietnamese teens survived and were captured. From their interrogation, division intelligence theorized that these adolescent attackers had been deployed simply to camouflage the three elite divisions of NVA regulars that were encamped just over the border in Cambodia.

Brenskie conjectured that the North Vietnamese command hierarchy had chosen to slaughter their young, inexperienced comrades just for the purpose of deception, a stratagem to give a false tactical impression to the U.S./South Vietnam coalition forces. A tragic attempt to disguise the obvious.

Barnes anguished about the stark contrast between America's reverence for life and the apparent lack of such in a Communist world. The NVA had not expected any of these young boys to live beyond the first wave of battle. How sad.

What a devilish plan of subterfuge to conceal an army's true objective, a secret build-up in Cambodia. American recon patrols may have been getting too close to the truth about this growing phalanx of forces. Somewhere over the border, buried beneath the ground, was an underworld of caves and interconnecting tunnels with storage depots, hospital rooms, and residential cubbyholes. First indications were that these structures existed too deep for any aerial bombardment to cause their collapse. This chain of community, often three stories deep, had to be vast and spread out. But where specifically? The question turning over and over in Barnes' mind was, "Would allied forces dare to cross into Cambodian territory and go after the enemy hiding there?"

CHAPTER 17

THE SIGN OF THE CROSS UNDER ATTACK

Wave after wave of fury would come over Adam Barnes every time he recalled the attempted perpetration of a hoax by Hanoi. Throwing raw recruits onto a fortified landing zone was like firing for false effect. They were just boys, not pawns for some transient battlefield trickery.

Another breach of the proprieties of war by the enemy similarly stoked more rage in Barnes. The Geneva Convention established a Code in 1864 which later was revised to protect the sick, the wounded, the captured, and the dead during wartime. The sign for safe conduct in these situations was the "Red Cross." Just as prisoners walking with their hands raised in surrender fell under protective custody of the code, hospitals, ambulances, and aircraft which bore the cross emblem were to be exempt from attack too. These large decals were evident in Vietnam on MEDEVAC helicopters and on "cracker box" ambulances, one of which Barnes had in his unit. The identifying design embodied a background block of white highlighted with the red cross in the center. Unfortunately such a bold symbol made a striking target for anyone who deliberately chose to ignore the Geneva Accord.

It was a well demarcated, readily noticeable bull's-eye for any object on which it was displayed.

During the aftermath of the outpost attack on the Cambodian border, the North Vietnamese applied an alarming new strategy. As a MEDEVAC helicopter took off from the clearing of LZ Brass and began to climb up over the triple-canopy jungle, a surface-to-air rocket came roaring up colliding head-on with the chopper fuselage. No one survived.

Multiple liftoffs of other Huey helicopters had occurred that morning but only the MEDEVAC was targeted for attack. This was the second such incident since the Tet Offensive and signaled the possibility of a new enemy tactic. In the past, ambulances had been fired upon sporadically but never any MEDEVAC aircraft. When a third rocket-propelled grenade attack was confirmed as a near miss on another First Cav dust-off, the targeting tactic against medical choppers was corroborated.

The Geneva Convention provided a worthless shield for any MEDEVAC venture. The mission of evacuating the wounded from the field had evolved to a greater level of peril for pilots. Yet fully briefed about the new stratagem of the enemy, daring young men continued to make the dangerous dust-off runs even in the midst of an ongoing fight; but with one minor artistic adjustment.

The U.S. Army was committed to maintaining the Geneva requirements for identifying medical aircraft, but it was quite clever with a small alteration in the pattern of painting. The Code called for a red plus sign to be emblazoned on a bold white background on all medical vehicles or transports. Step one was to tone down the brilliance of the red cross to a maroon shade. The ingenious part was step two—in order to fulfill the white background stipulation, the border around the dark red cross outlined just one inch of white paint. From a distance, this combination made the color scheme a much less distinct center point for sighting. It did not stop the enemy sniper or RPG rifleman from firing on MEDEVAC helicopters, but it did reduce the number of successful attacks.

Captain Barnes frequently flew from landing zone to landing zone in a light observation chopper nicknamed a "LOCH." It was a small helicopter with dual front seats and an interwoven strap bench in the compartment behind the pilots. The LOCH was essentially unarmed and used for airborne observation of combat. This aircraft was agile and fast, able to maneuver just above the tree line safely. Since it had these attributes, it could be utilized to draw fire from the enemy and thus expose their positions for counter assault. These flying bubbles were not marked with any medical insignia though medical personnel traveled in them regularly.

Chief warrant officer Mason Huneycutt had been the air chauffeur for Adam Barnes going on three months. Cutty, as he was called, loved to fly and in another era of flight he would have been one of those fearless young men barnstorming across the U.S. in their flying machines circa 1920. Barnes was always tense in the air; Huneycutt was laid back. He was married to his machine and a deeper joy in navigating the airways no one could have.

Pilot and passenger had taken off just after breakfast. The morning air was sultry so ascending to a higher altitude brought comfort from the heavy heat. The flight out to LZ Caroline was uneventful until Barnes and Huneycutt neared the Cambodian border. Radio transmissions indicated a barrage of gunfire had broken out just south of the LZ. A curtain of artillery detonations was visible on the ground below, but the whistling sound of high angle rounds piercing the upper atmosphere caused Cutty to peel off to the east to let the artillery shells have the southern airspace.

A company of CAV infantry was returning from a night patrol operation around the perimeter of LZ Caroline when it was surprised by a squad of NVA regulars who popped up out of nowhere. A fierce firefight broke out on the edge of a thick jungle tree grove. It lasted less than thirty minutes and ended as abruptly as it had begun.

From the vantage point of the LOH (a more formal lettering designation for the light observation helicopter) in which Barnes was flying, he could see a few black pajama-clad soldiers fleeing in the forested terrain to the southeast. Then they just vanished leaving the pursuing American grunts crouching in an open field, mystified at the sudden disappearance of their quarry.

Barnes' helicopter spiraled down from above the LZ like a roller coaster car descending on single rail loops. On the ground, Barnes joined the camp battalion surgeon and began the triage process of preparing the wounded for medevacuation.

A minor scrap was continuing less than a click from the perimeter wire and Cobra gunships were circling over the field of battle. Flying among the gunships was another LOCH attempting to pinpoint the tunnel entrances into which the NVA scampered after initiating contact. This helicopter was acting as a forward observer for artillery support while at the same time trying to entice the enemy into firing a revelatory shot. It worked!

Suddenly AK-47 tracers arched out of the jungle canopy striking the LOCH. The helicopter began to rotate slowly then more rapidly. It dipped east in an erratic pattern of flight and flew toward the LZ landing pads. The aircraft did not make it. First hovering outside the barbed wire, it then landed awkwardly and hard on its runners in an adjacent clearing.

Barnes was in the process of immobilizing a wounded soldier's head, using the man's own boots as a neck brace to improve respiration and prevent any latent spinal cord trauma, when the copter came down less than twenty yards away. Through the swirling puffs of dust he could see the seemingly slow motion bounce and final thump down of the aircraft. Everyone in the area attempted to duck below the prop gust, crawling and sprawling out on the ground.

Within minutes a medic came running up in search of help. He explained that both pilots in the LOCH had been hit with rifle fire up through the floor of the cockpit; one was hit in the shoulder and the other in the foot. Under those circumstances it had been an astounding feat of aviating skill to land that chopper without crashing.

Barnes finished bandaging his patient and headed off with the medic. After some initial stabilization, temporary wound dressing, and morphine injections for pain, both pilots were evacuated.

As the frenzied pace of acute trauma care slowed and the sound of outgoing artillery rounds lessened, Barnes found his mind replaying the landing of that LOCH helicopter. To Barnes, the circumstances which had forced the calamity within that copter were most troubling. These two pilots flew in the very same type of aircraft Barnes used in missions over the III Corps. He sat in the left seat and Huneycutt controlled the plane from the right. Barnes had never considered until this moment the reality of what could happen if Cutty were shot or incapacitated while in flight. Barnes was not a pilot. He may have been an Army sky trooper; but he could not fly anything in the sky, except maybe a kite.

The next day as Barnes and Huneycutt lifted off for Phuoc Vinh headquarters, Adam broached the subject of emergencies with his pilot. "Cutty, if something were to happen to you while we are in flight, what should I do?"

Huneycutt wryly replied, "Pray."

"No, I'm serious. I don't know how to fly this thing."

Huneycutt's response exhibited an airman's overconfidence. "Nothing's gonna happen."

"I know but what if it did?" Barnes replied. "What should I do? Can you teach me to fly?"

Again with superstitious fervor, "Nothin's gonna happen to me!"

Dr. Barnes persisted.

"Okay," said Huneycutt, "if something happens to me, this is what you can do."

Barnes was all eyes and ears.

"First, you grab that joystick," pointing to the second control stick located between Barnes' legs, "and pretend you're trying to balance this crate on a tightrope. Slowly, S-L-O-W-L-Y move the stick in the opposite direction of the chopper's lean until you have the ship balanced. Don't move anything fast up here."

"How will I know it's balanced?" asked Barnes.

"Watch the horizon. You'll know."

Cutty showed Barnes how to do it and then let him try.

"Watch the horizon, not me. Have you got it balanced?" Cutty asked.

"I think so," Barnes replied.

"Know so! And don't touch the pedals!"

Huneycutt's next instruction was crucial.

"Now reach over with your right hand, palm open and down, and gradually depress the throttle bar." The throttle looked like a Harley Davidson motorcycle handle on a pipe extending at a 45-degree angle out of the floor box between them.

"Don't grip or twist the throttle. Just slowly press it down until the chopper starts to descend," warned Huneycutt. He demonstrated the maneuver to Barnes and then encouraged him to give it a try.

Hesitantly, Barnes reached above the throttle, made contact with the center of his palm, and pressed downward. Ever so slightly the whirlybird started to descend. A patch of wispy, white clouds was directly in their path. Blue sky above, another bank of clouds below. The downturn was controlled…a whiff of haze and they passed through…more clouds were coming up and the chopper was gliding down. In the clouds briefly, then back out. The ground was visible…and it was coming up. The chopper continued to come down on a sloping trajectory.

Barnes was exhilarated with the parting of the last cloud. He thought to himself, "Look at me, I'm flying!" The features of the ground grew more distinct as they were coming up and the chopper was coursing down.

Barnes snuck a peek at Huneycutt who was calmly sitting there with a prankish grin on his face.

"Now *I'm* doing this, right? You're not helping me?" asked Barnes.

"Keep your eye on the horizon. It's all you, I promise," Cutty replied.

The ground was coming up and the chopper was going down.

Ground, up, chopper, down...up...down. The oft loquacious Huneycutt was strangely silent. Not a word! Tension in the cabin bulb was mounting for Barnes.

"Okay, what do I do when we get down to the ground?" Barnes asked urgently as nervous sweat began to pump from the pores on his brow.

Huneycutt was cool as a cucumber without a hint of humor in his voice, staring sternly at the ground now just a couple hundred feet below.

"You crash!"

After a brief pause for effect, Cutty took hold of the joystick. "Your best chance of survival is to let the bird just drive itself into the ground. Don't attempt any hovering or maneuvering the pedals, stick, or throttle. If you tried any of those things, you might explode on impact. Just drive it into the ground."

Barnes thought he had learned how to fly. All he had learned to do was how to crash. He prayed a flash prayer of thanks.

Cutty was back in control.

CHAPTER 18

A LIFE LAID DOWN

Dusk was settling in over the Phuoc Vinh base camp with the usual gray clouds and magnificent sunbursts. Captain Barnes had just left the aid station and was headed to the tactical operations center (TOC) to speak with the executive officer (XO). The topic would be sandbags again and their inadequate supply in the field. Whenever CAV medics moved to a new firebase, they were being required to empty sandbags in order to refill them at the new LZ. Apparently allotments for the CAV of this most significant defense item were scarce at the time. "So much for being the wealthiest nation in the world when it comes to supplying its army in wartime," Barnes scoffed to himself.

At the TOC the doctor angled through the L-shaped maze of sheet metal and high dirt-retaining walls. As he reached the fortified doorway, incoming rockets and mortar rounds began raining out of the twilight sky. The impacting whomps were whipping particles of dust and dirt up into a visual haze. Barnes ducked into a back corner of the TOC, crouching into a ball against the wall. A direct hit on that structure seemed imminent. For Barnes, being hunched on one's haunches was not a position of power.

Hunkering down was humbling and only added to his feeling of helplessness.

The radio was squawking with follow-up reports on the attack. It turned out to be only an assault of missiles and mortars, no men, no subsequent probings on the perimeter—just another nuisance bombardment. But far too accurate on Hard Charger headquarters.

As Barnes exited the TOC to check on his men at the aid station, he passed multiple smoldering fires being extinguished by his comrades. He recollected that he had just been walking this path seconds before the first impaction. Timing and placement had been critical for him, but what about his staff?

On reaching the dispensary, Barnes headed to the rear bed chambers of the station medics. The two specialists were not in the building—he was relieved. They had been playing cards there when he had left.

Barnes shot out the back door. On the opposite side of the aid station, the crackerbox ambulance had been parked. (Barnes had hoped to upgrade this World War II vintage vehicle into a traveling OR for minor surgery at MEDCAPs.) An exploding mortar shell had made a direct hit on the "old relic," and it was still on fire.

Barnes grabbed a fire extinguisher from inside the cab door and started spraying the flames swirling beneath the chassis. They were dangerously close to the gas tank. An explosion of fuel could damage the dispensary by starting a secondary fire on the wooden structure.

Arriving at that moment, the executive officer ripped open the front door and jumped into the driver's seat. Reaching through the flames he was able to release the emergency brake and pop the gear shift into neutral. Both hands sustained second-degree burns. His effort allowed other personnel to push the vehicle away from the side of the clinic, and eventually the various blazes were snuffed out. The ambulance was ultimately irreparable, but the aid station was spared.

When Captain Barnes saw that pieces of shrapnel had sliced through the station's front room screens, he felt vindicated for leaving the sandbag wall beside the living quarters intact after the IG inspection was cancelled. Barnes believed that being in nonconformity for safety reasons had proven to be far superior to having design uniformity for the sake of a better grade in some gratuitous field review. ***Vietnam was not a game. It was a war.***

As Barnes bandaged the XO's hands, the major's simple, "You were right!" declaration was inwardly satisfying to the doctor. No more was ever said about the sandbag controversy.

The same night of the Phuoc Vinh attack, another firebase, LZ Grant, had come under an all out assault, with very severe consequences. At one point the NVA assailants had breached the defensive perimeter and 1st/30th artillerymen were sighting down the barrels of their 155s and directly firing at the onrushing sappers. The NVA troops were forced back, but one costly casualty occurred.

The next wave of attack was preceded by walking volleys of mortar rounds through the howitzer emplacements. When there was a lull in the fighting, Medic Chris Alvarez sprang over the earthen barriers into the gun pit to assist the wounded. The enemy had tactically paused their shelling to allow the influx of support personnel to take place. Then they opened up with a new round of mortar fire on the same site with zeroed-in accuracy. Whomp, whomp, whomp!

Since the soil and sandbags were of no value in the case of a direct hit, Alvarez was vulnerable inside the gun pit. He heard the distant plunk from the tube, but not the overhead whoosh. The impact concussion shook one howitzer from its steel anchoring stakes. As Alvarez kneeled to give aid to a fallen soldier, he was seriously wounded in the back by a large piece of shrapnel. The howitzer beside which he ministered was heaved up and on its side pinning the injured medic with its muzzle into the mud. His final words were inadvertently picked up on the tape recorder which someone had tossed into the pit when the fighting started (a common practice among gunmen to record the sounds of war for later amusement in the aftermath of battle).

When Chris Alvarez was approached by the battery's first sergeant, his voice could be heard on the pocket recorder to whisper, "Top, I'm a goner. Save someone else."

Private First Class Chris Alvarez had made the ultimate sacrifice, dying in an effort to save another.

The gunmen of the 1st/30th Artillery were not just acquaintances in need of medical care. To this medic they were friends for whom he would die to save. Even though near DEROS, he chose dutifully to respond at great peril to himself and would be remembered as a hero to those with whom he served.

Against army protocol (only commanding officers were supposed to write to next of kin), but consistent with his character, Captain Barnes sent his own note of condolence to the parents of Private Alverez in Texas. The letter included a scripture from the Bible, most fitting for this medic. "Greater love hath no man than this, that he lay down his life for his friends." (John 15:13)

From that time on, the battalion surgeon prayed nightly that this would be the only missive of sympathy he would have to write in this war.

One of the results of this increase in the number of over-the-border hit and runs by the NVA divisions based in Cambodia was a more expansive strategy for Division Artillery (DIVARTY). Massive firepower support for the First Cav would require a spreading out for 1st/30th Battalion and the other artillery groups in the short term.

Artillery personnel had become increasingly adept at moving from CAV firebase to CAV firebase, most of which were in isolated jungle forest regions where huge divots would slice through the terrain to provide clear and open ground. In order to make the necessary adjustments ordered by DIVARTY, the individual batteries would be divided. Batteries of six howitzers would split into two units of three guns or three units of two guns. Of course, medical coverage to the now dispersed gunmen would have to be expanded creatively too.

For this reason, Captain Barnes knew he would need to replace the lost medic of Alpha Battery. He decided to reassign a member of his own base staff in the interim, Specialist Vic Allen, a California-educated medical tech. He had not been trained as an army field medic, but was quite competent for the task. Under the circumstances he agreed to go voluntarily even knowing that with his military occupational specialty he could not be forced to go out into the field as a medic.

Captain Barnes instituted a plan whereby he himself would go out to LZ Grant and cover the duties of the battery medic who was killed until a replacement could be assigned from 15th Med. He would send Allen to be the medic with the three guns of Alpha Battery being sectioned out to leave LZ Grant. The new mission for this unit was to provide heavy tube artillery support from the mountain top base of Nui Ba Dinh. This was in the III Corps region inhabited by the Montagnards. The Christian Children's Foundation orphanage, The Shepherd of the Hill, was also located in the neighboring Phuoc Long province.

Adam Barnes was fascinated that as a matter of course whenever any major combat engagement with North Vietnamese forces took place, company commanders could expect a swarming of division staff to the battle site within twenty-four hours or less. Being the senior medical officer present on LZ Grant after the most recent attack, Captain Barnes was called upon to present a medical status report to the visiting brass as part of the battle assessment briefing.

The First Cav division commander, Major General Robert Benning, had arrived at this forward firebase at first light. The briefing was scheduled for 1000 hours and was to be held in a canvas pavilion erected for that purpose. When Barnes ducked into the tent he noticed the major general seated alone behind a table flanked by his brigade generals who were positioned front, left, and right for face-to-face access.

General Benning was an impressive figure to Barnes, who perceived no panic in the General, just a calm and reflective bearing.

His manner was all military down to the preciseness of his rolled up uniform sleeves. His steel-pot helmet rested on the table. He listened respectfully to his brigade leaders as they separately provided their analysis of what had happened the day before and what might be expected from the enemy across III Corps in the immediate future. The views were varied, some narrow-minded, some naïve, some too simplistic from Barnes' perspective. The commander heard them all without expression or interruption. The only distraction was the occasional prop wash of a helicopter coming or going, blowing gusts of dust under the tent flaps.

The doctor was concerned. The mission forest was being obscured by the variety of tactical trees being expressed by brigade staff members. What was the big picture beneath the jungle canopy?

When all had spoken, General Benning stood up. After a brief pause and an eerie sense of silence, he began to speak. He delineated every possible strategy upon which the enemy could embark; and to each action he laid out a comprehensive response.

Captain Barnes conceded that in spite of the Brigade level's limited scope of vision, the major general had seen the whole landscape. He understood the dynamics of a propaganda war—attack for the purpose of maiming and killing for headlines or the body count effect. Yet he sensed something bigger was behind this seemingly isolated border assault—a distraction from the supply and personnel build-up of Cambodia in general or a diversion from a specific NVA staging area in the very region toward which the First Air Cav was probing. His plan? The allied forces in III Corps would prepare offenses and defenses for every eventuality.

This approach was encouraging to Barnes who likened it to the day-to-day practices of pre-season basketball training at Duke. Preparation was made in advance for every contingency the coaches could think of before the first game's ball was ever tossed by the referee. The First Cav would prepare for every possibility. They would be prepared to adapt and to execute under any circumstances. Every option was on the table *except for one.*

CHAPTER 19

CONSULTATION WITH A COLONEL

The medical portion of the LZ Grant briefing before the commanding officers was routine for Barnes. It was his realm of responsibility so he kept it short and sweet. The wounded had been treated and those requiring more extensive care had been MEDEVACed out. One combat medic had been killed and arrangements for his replacement were in the works. The fighting condition of the men at this firebase was good from a mental and medical standpoint. A little rest would help. Barnes surprised himself at how matter of fact he was. It was like giving a student précis at a clinical pathology conference in med school.

Barnes' attendance at this assemblage proved manifestly educational. While gleaning new insights about the command chain and its politics, he became better informed about the CAV's game plan for Cambodia. The briefing also facilitated an introduction to division Chief of Staff, Colonel Casey King.

At the close of that morning's session, after the officers were dismissed, a tall, lanky "bird colonel" approached Captain Barnes, intercepting him just outside the assembly tent.

"Captain, may I have a word with you?"

Barnes grew tense as he replied in the affirmative with a

salute. It was soon clear that Colonel King was a down-to-earth guy in spite of being regular army and having superior rank. Of note to Barnes were the wrinkled lines of his facial expression. He was inwardly troubled.

The two officers headed over to the mess hall for coffee then to a row of sandbags which made up the wall revetment of a helicopter pad. In time Barnes would learn that the colonel was a West Point grad and that this was his second tour in Vietnam. He had even played a little round ball intercollegiately in the early 50s while a cadet.

Sports reminiscing was not the reason that the colonel had singled Barnes out for this meeting. The agenda was medical in nature, and personal. Casey King had received a letter recently from his wife that informed him that she may have multiple sclerosis (MS). King wanted to know what the doctor could tell him about the disease.

Yet still tentative, the diagnosis had been arrived at by a process of elimination. The primary symptoms were abnormal sensations in the extremities associated with muscle weakness and dizzy spells. These symptoms, which his wife had kept secret for some time, could fit many other benign conditions, but most of those entities had been ruled out by the usual screening tests. The colonel was asking with his head about treatment options, disabilities, remissions, and prognosis, if in fact it was MS. Unfortunately, his heart, probably awash with a feeling of powerlessness, despaired for a more hopeful diagnosis.

All Barnes knew was that MS was some strange neurological disorder about which he had only read in textbooks. He acknowledged to the colonel that he had never encountered MS in pediatrics. However, he did recall one article that linked the symptoms to scattered lesions in the white matter of the brain. What caused the lesions was only speculation. (Barnes wished he could rephrase his responses more positively in spite of the inherent insensitivity of technical terms.) King appreciated the shared information, his facial expression depicting a slight sense of relief. Clearly though, the burden of command responsibilities in a war *here* compounded his concern for his wife *there*.

After a sip of coffee and a brief lull in their conversation, Colonel King confided that he was contemplating resignation from his commission after he returned to the States. Barnes was frankly caught off guard by his candor. King went on to say that he did not want to have another hardship tour away from his family, even with just eight years to go before reaching his retirement "twenty." He had missed the privilege of watching his three children grow up. Now his wife's health condition was an additional factor in his deliberation about resigning.

After a long delay because of several Cobra attack helicopters taking off, Barnes spoke up with a change-the-subject abruptness. Awkward? Yes, but probably appropriate considering the trust personally exhibited by the colonel in discussing his family and his future.

"Sir, may I ask you a question about the morning briefing with General Benning and then have permission to speak freely in comment?" Barnes asked.

Colonel King nodded.

"Sir, if we know that the North Vietnamese are in certain uninhabited regions across the border in Cambodia, and if we know within a reasonable doubt the location of the Ho Chi Minh Trail south out of Laos, why do we not block it with bombs? Big Bombs? Tactical Nuclear bombs?"

Barnes studied his confidant's face for signs of his being unintentionally out of order as he continued. "Regarding the underground supply bunkers and the troop tunnel networks, these would be crushed and the earth cleared and compacted. It would seem that a radioactive curtain between the countries would provide a prolonged safety cushion between the NVA regulars in Cambodia and the fledgling ARVN forces on the South Vietnam side."

There was a pause on King's behalf. Then, quite matter-of-factly, he said, "It's a political and a public relations strategy for now rather than a pound the enemy into submission and peace approach. The world may not be ready for a nuclear response here."

Barnes boldly blurted out, "Why send a young soldier on search and destroy missions, when one well-placed super bomb could bring about the same effect? I believe tactical nukes would save lives just as in World War II…lives on both sides."

Colonel King was silently reflective. Even if he agreed, he instinctively knew to be very cautious on the subject of nuclear weapons, tactical or otherwise.

The division generals and their staffs were assembling beside Huey helicopters, already coming hot and poised to leave before lunch. The various company commanders who would remain on the LZ had operational preparations to make for whatever might come out of the jungle against them that afternoon or out of the darkness that night. "Charlie" was notorious for returning to the scene of the crime.

As Colonel King rose to head for his waiting ride, he thanked Dr. Barnes for his kind consultation.

The captain stood, saluted and uttered, "Sir, I will pray that things go well for your wife."

The colonel glanced back over his shoulder in acknowledgement that he had heard the physician's pledge.

Over the next three days and nights in spite of the border remaining without any offensive incidents, the alert level stayed on high. Mental concentration was exhausting. Rest was rare. Yet the enemy had vanished—either they had totally withdrawn to huddle below the horizon or they were secretly waiting beneath the surface of the soil to attack again. No sightings were made from overflying helicopters, field binoculars, or night scopes. No concentrations of combatants could be found anywhere.

The assault at LZ Grant, along with other sporadic bombardments in Fishhook, was being interpreted publicly as simple probings or staged diversions. The intelligence experts of S-2 were studying the reconnaissance data and scanning aerial photographs for answers.

The body-count box scores after this and other head-to-head confrontations with the Viet Cong insurgents consistently revealed a ratio of ten to one—ten enemy fighters killed for every single American loss. These war-score statistics represented a streak of games won on specific battlefields. Yet for the one casualty, it would always be a tragic loss. Barnes was hardening, finding it increasingly difficult to associate the adjective, "tragic," in reference to the ten on the other side. That he would even entertain the thought of a nuclear option was no shock to Barnes considering the breadth of his growing wrath for the enemy who had just killed the one out of the ten of his field medics.

Barnes was anxious for the political transformation in the

provinces of III Corps to accelerate before he lost another medic, a number *two*. Progress in the pacification process was happening, but in the trees of grief, Barnes could not see the ever-expanding forest. For the first time in 172 years of Vietnam history, free elections had taken place in the rural hamlets. Villages that at one time were terrorized by the Viet Cong were now experiencing a breath of liberty. The tyranny of untruth was incrementally being replaced by truth and trust.

The peace, though fragile, was freedom-based—freedom to choose their own leaders and freedom of those leaders to challenge authoritarian propaganda. Could peace be sustained? All the Vietnam villagers wanted was to be left alone to live the culture of their ancestors in peace. No one could guarantee such an environment, but if security existed in a village, then the newly planted freedom trees could take root creating the new freedom forest. And in the new forest the process of bearing fruit would begin. "Life, liberty, and the pursuit of happiness."

After one week and the assignment of two new medics to 1st/30th Artillery, Captain Barnes and Specialist Vic Allen were reunited in Phuoc Vinh. Barnes debriefed Allen about his service on Nui Ba Dinh and inquired how the staff at the mission orphanage were doing. Allen gave Barnes an update and then related how he met someone there who said they knew the doctor back in the States. The specialist queried, "Do you remember a nurse named Claire Marshall?"

CHAPTER 20

HALF DOZEN DOWN TOWARD DEROS

The screen door of the aid station could be heard to bang open and around the office partition Sergeant Tam rushed to an abrupt and winded halt. He had just returned from a brief weekend leave to visit his wife and two-year-old daughter in Saigon. His face was flushed and his demeanor was a phase of frantic. Unbeknownst to anyone in the room, over the weekend, a significant barrage of rockets had been unleashed down on the suburban outskirts of Saigon. One rocket had come dangerously close to Tam's house while he and his family were sleeping on the same block, just doors away. The resultant fires forced everyone chaotically out into the street. After extensive damage to the neighboring structures, the fires were extinguished. Tam's rest and relaxation (R&R) had been spent helping neighbors sift through the smoldering ashes of their huts and houses and moving his wife and daughter farther out of the city to a village where his in-laws lived.

Upon Tam's return to Phuoc Vinh duty, a fellow ARVN interpreter had shared the rumor circulating that Captain Barnes had been assigned back to the 15th Medical Battalion for his second six months of Vietnam duty. That tidbit of talk coupled with his devastating weekend experience had triggered the explosive entrance to the aid station.

In rapid-fire succession, emphasizing with forceful, finger-pointing gestures, Tam blurted out, "You have DEROS! Vic has DEROS!"

One by one he pointed around the room. "Captain Barnes has DEROS!" His gesticulations were emphatic toward every person in the room.

He then placed his index finger toward his own chest. "But me, no DEROS! After you gone...I have stay!"

Tam's rant was accurate and revelatory. Each singular soldier from the United States had a "365 and a wakeup." DEROS day... Date Estimated Return from OverSeas (as noted in each soldier's 201 personnel file). The war would be over for them. On that day they would take the "freedom bird" home to American soil. Yet such would not be the case for the battalion interpreter. He and his young family would have to abide and endure. To that point the clinic staff had been insensitive to the world of the Vietnamese. Selfishly, they had chosen to be oblivious to Tam's obvious plight. Every member in that room had no immediate family for whom they would be called upon to protect day and night. Their war would end at DEROS, his would not. From that moment on, the question of why the U.S. was there took on a more personal meaning. It was families like Tam's, their future and freedom, for which the American soldier would inevitably be fighting. For some it would be a willing sacrifice for a foreign friend; for others, it would be a day-to-day duty just to tough it out until DEROS.

The rumor Tam had heard about Captain Barnes was true. The doctor, having completed his half-a-DEROS of days, was in fact, being reassigned to 15th Medical Battalion. Since the headquarters company was just across the air strip, he would still be stationed in Phuoc Vinh. His replacement at 1st/30th Artillery, Doctor Fred Arnold, had already received orders for the new position having served his first six months at 24th Evacuation Hospital. Doctor Arnold trained and graduated from the medical school at Ohio State University and had completed his internship at Akron General Hospital. However, his hometown was the farming community of Clayton, North Carolina, near Raleigh.

As a professional courtesy, Doctor Barnes arranged to take Doctor Arnold on a whirlwind helicopter tour of all the present CAV firebase LZs where 1st/30th medics were practicing field medicine. Of course, Barnes had an ulterior motive for this "farewell tour" across III Corps. His culminating stop would be Nui Ba Dinh—and a reunion with Claire Marshall.

Fred was a funny guy, a man with a marvelous gift for telling stories. His dry wit and southern homespun humor would fit in well with the artillery guys. During a layover before the last-leg flight to Nui Ba Dinh, Barnes asked Arnold if he had ever played a round of golf at Akron's Firestone Country Club where the World Series of Golf was held since 1962.

Arnold answered, "Once."

He then related how he was playing in a pick-up foursome between two doctors from the University of Michigan and two doctors from the Ohio State University. The head of the internal medicine department at Akron General and one of his residents were avid Wolverine alumni. Another staff physician and Arnold were both Buckeye graduates. The competition was described as fierce but friendly between the forever arch-rivals.

Arnold continued to recount his experience on the Firestone course. On the twelfth hole, a par five, the "Big Blue" department head drove an errant shot into the rough. In retrieving his ball using his three iron as a scythe in the long underbrush, he inadvertently stirred up a nest of yellow jacket wasps. These sand daubers were so aggressive that the physician's knit golf shirt was plastered with a layer of bees, stinging him repeatedly. It was a relentless attack. The golfer's reaction to the venom was instantaneous and systemic. Within minutes he was swelling up, having trouble breathing, and going into shock as his blood pressure plummeted. He and his colleagues easily diagnosed anaphylaxis. Believing he was approaching death, the victim, in a wheezing voice, asked his friends to contact his wife. Since his home was on a golf fairway nearby, she arrived in a golf cart before the ambulance did.

The doctor was so certain of his impending death, that he confessed all of his sexual indiscretions to his wife, one particular dalliance being especially egregious because it involved a neighbor's wife. He was plaintively pleading with his spouse to forgive him when the emergency services team arrived and administered an injection of epinephrine.

As Barnes listened to the account he reflected upon his own encounter with the VC Bees. He decided he would give the new battalion surgeon a "bee-briefing" after the golf story was completed.

Arnold's narrative had a fascinating finish with a twist. The doctor golfer did not die. He survived thanks to the EpiPen shot. However, because of the confessions, his wife chose to divorce him and she took him "for all he was worth, including the house along the fairway of the Firestone South course." (Barnes could not decipher if he was being regaled with a true tale or just another tall tale by Arnold.) Either way, the new doctor had managed to divert Barnes' attention effectively and humorously throughout his final "rounds" trip to the field.

———

The LOCH chopper was touching down on the pinnacle pod of Nui Ba Dinh as Arnold completed another yarn. Barnes' mind returned to the dual mission of why they had come. After formally introducing the new doctor to the battery commander and the field medic, Barnes headed around to the opposite side of the mountain. He scampered over a series of boulders which jutted out of the summit. He bounded back and forth down the traversing path which led to the Shepherd of The Hill orphanage which was perched beyond the lower crest of the crater top. It was mid-afternoon.

The mission-school sessions had just let out for the day when Barnes came over the ridge which to that point had concealed a full view of the front porch of the main meeting house. The three tiers of steps were bustling with children of all ages. Like baby eaglets pressing around their mother hen for food and affection, they were nestling up close to a young woman dressed in a close-fitting white silk tunic which covered her ao dai (white trousers). She had just stood up from the top step to reenter the building when the children transferred their attention from her to the soldier behind them on the knoll.

Standing on the platformed porch, Claire Marshall turned and tilted her head as she moved from under the eaves back to the edge of the landing. Her long, lovely locks were gone, having been sacrificed for a more convenient and manageable pageboy cut. She peered across the horizon from beneath her golden bangs as she squinted into the sun. Using her hand to shade her eyes from the afternoon glare, Claire recognized Adam Barnes first from his pigeon-toed, athletic gait, but confirmed his identity when he removed his helmet to tuck it smartly under his arm. The students parted like the Red Sea so that the line of sight between the two American friends was unobstructed.

Captain Barnes paused at the bottom of the steps. The children were snatching peeks at his face, then at Claire, and back again. She spoke something in French and the children relaxed— some with grins, some with broad smiles, and some who were older, with cautious discerning looks.

"Strange meeting you here," said Barnes in his inimitable, awkward manner, not really knowing what to say.

Claire smiled winsomely. "Doctor Barnes, I presume."

Adam climbed the planked stairs. They hugged as a brother and a sister might, Barnes attempting to restrict the contact of his dust-covered flak jacket against the white of her smock. Claire's body closed the gap, and her head and shoulders engaged his shoulder and chest as if two young people were embracing to dance. He gently lifted her to her tiptoes and slowly released her down. Particles of clay outlined an imprint of a red bib along the points where their clothing touched.

Claire brushed the dust with one stroke of her left hand. "How are you doing?"

Barnes' mind did not even register the inquiry at first. His focus was transfixed on following the gentle sweep of her fingers across the white silk background of her tunic top. No ring!

"Oh, fine. But more importantly, what are *you* doing here?"

Barnes replied, while contemplating logical explanations for the absence of the engagement ring.

"It's a long story. I sent you a letter but I guess it never reached you. I only had an APO number. After that remarkable coincidence of meeting your medic up here, every time a helicopter landed, I wondered if you could be on it. How much time do you have to visit?" Claire asked excitedly.

Adam rapidly processed his schedule options which were few being a soldier, not a civilian. Considering the time of day he figured he had about one hour or less. He toyed with the idea of conjuring up a pediatric consultation need at the orphanage; but that would be lying and he would not lie. Maybe evade, but not lie.

Adam was happy as the day was long to have any time with Claire, but his day was growing short. So many questions to ask; so few moments to ask them.

He finally but begrudgingly responded, "I have about an hour before I have to head out, but maybe I can arrange to come back for some follow-up MEDCAP clinics after I get to my new duty assignment." Barnes explained his realignment with 15th Medical Battalion in Phuoc Vinh for his second six months in country.

The two friends slipped away from the crush of children into the dining area of the orphanage. Claire tactfully instructed the clinging kids who were still following that they should remain outside and that she would be back to play in a short time. Inside the starkly furnished structure, she and Adam sat across from each other at one end of a long table.

Adam's first question. "I probably shouldn't ask, but I don't see a ring. Still engaged to that professor at Stanford?"

"No," was her response as she looked away in an attempt to conceal her pained expression. "We broke it off when I got this opportunity to come overseas to the mission field. Charles and I didn't see eye to eye on the missionary thing—the timing or the location. Too dangerous, foolish, and all that. Differences of opinion over the matter strained our relationship. We both were heading in opposite directions. We became estranged. I suppose it was inevitable."

Feeling his own tension level mounting, Barnes brusquely interjected with a stutter.

"I....I...I have to agree with your fiancé. He is right. It is too dangerous for an American woman over here, missionary or otherwise."

Claire sharply countered: *"Et tu, Barne?"*

Then as if defending again her decision to be there, she added, "Adam, the mission calling was real to me. You remember, I always wanted to be a medical missionary of some type. I knew about the Christian Children's Foundation from my work with those Vietnamese orphans back in Oakland. I started praying for God to give me a willing spirit to obey the call I'd experienced years ago—and He did!"

As she related her testimony, Claire was becoming more and more animated (and more and more appealing to Adam). Her enthusiasm was elating. Her expression, radiant. She glowed with conviction for her calling.

Claire continued, "The very day after I prayerfully promised God I'd go anywhere He wanted me to, an opportunity came. A nursing magazine arrived in the mail with an advertisement recruiting Christian nurses for overseas service. I took it as a sign. Like Gideon, I fleeced the Lord for an answer."

Claire noticed that Adam looked askance with a subtle lowering tilt of his head.

"Oh, I know that's probably wrong to do, but then again the challenge presented itself. I researched it and here I am!" She slowly curved her lips upward into a faint smile.

Barnes listened, wanting to interrupt again, but uncharacteristically restrained himself. He sensed Claire needed this catharsis. Internally he had already decided to back off from any further chauvinistic retorts about war zones and women. Deep down, Barnes was impressed by Claire's dedication to a spiritual calling. He had admired her integrity of faith ever since those days at summer camp.

Tempering his compulsion to confront Claire about the perils of Vietnam was the glorious discovery that she was unengaged, unattached, available and here. Adam was overwhelmed with a strange inner joy, but on the exterior he exhibited a state of platonic detachment regarding the matter of her broken relationship. In his reticence not to reveal his true feelings for Claire, Adam deliberately kept the conversation light.

"When did you arrive in country? How long is your mission tour? Is it like what you thought it would be?"

Barnes did what his "reserve" required. Cloaked with an impassive demeanor, he might have appeared insensitive to how Claire must have felt considering all the emotions which embody breaking an engagement. That was not the case. Barnes was not incapable of being affected by the suffering of others. He was, after all, a physician. Yet when it came to personal relationships and their potential for creating heartache, he would not risk the hurt of a broken heart.

In order for the door in his heart's emotional wall to be opened again, Adam would need a sign from God too—a sign that he would not get hurt. To assure such a painless result, Barnes was carefully reading Claire—her body language as well as her verbal response. In medicine he had been trained to discern beneath the external of his patients. Entrenched aloofness had hardened into another layer of guardedness in Barnes, a layer that would have to be chiseled away piece by piece.

"What did your folks have to say about your decisions?" It was an open-ended question from Barnes to keep the conversation going.

"Oh, they have been very supportive. They liked Charles, but the decision, they knew, was mine—in both instances, marriage and mission field. That's how they reared me. Long story short, Charles and I were changing in who we were. Our paths were no longer parallel. The separate life lines had crossed once, but we were growing farther and farther apart. Charles defined himself as a progressive humanist. I am a conservative Christian. Faith matters a great deal to me. You know the Good Book warns about 'unequally yoked marriages.'"

Claire smiled that smile which involved and enveloped her whole face, the winsome one that could light up a whole room. Barnes basked in the warmth of its cheerfulness.

"What's happening back home?" he asked.

"Anti-war and anti-military sentiment is growing, especially on the college campuses…a lot of frustration. The hateful climate at Bay Area schools is very shameful and divisive regarding the war."

Claire stared intently into Adam's eyes and with a soft, sympathetic tone she said, "I sincerely respect what you guys are trying to do here. The little time I've been on this mountain, I've learned a great deal. My heart goes out to these Montagnards and their children. They're caught in the middle. I pray that they can have the peace and freedom I have known. But war...."

Barnes could sense Claire's struggle with her ambivalent feelings. She still hated the violence of a military solution, but could appreciate what the American soldier was trying to do against tyranny. She did not agree with the rationale for this particular war but could respect those who had, by no choice of their own, been called up to fight it.

The compassionate conversation between Adam and Claire was interrupted by the sound of footsteps entering the room. A young teenage boy circled behind Claire and whispered in her ear. She responded briefly in a manner which Barnes could interpret as thank you in French. The message conveyed by the boy was that another American soldier was outside looking for "Dai-wi" Barnes. It was Cutty.

The chopper chauffeur had an instinct about weather and schedules. He was keenly attentive in assuring that "the trains maintained their timetables," planes and helicopters too—on time and on schedule both arriving and departing. In Cutty's mind it was "time to depart." His idiosyncrasies had kept him alive and out of any air incidents, beating the eight-month odds for most pilots before an accident or worse. Time to go meant time to go!

Adam Barnes gently grasped and pressed Claire's hands.

She caressingly repositioned them to enfold his hands inside hers. "Remember, the Lord is your Shepherd, and never forget that I pray for you every day." Her touch was endearing; her eyes glistened with tears.

Barnes slowly withdrew his hands from her clasp and mouthed, "Thanks," since his vocal cords seemed incapable of producing sound without breath.

The two friends stood. Barnes picked up his helmet from the table. Claire led the way from the room and out onto the porch. A gust of dust greeted them.

Cutty stood at the bottom of the steps. When he saw Claire he did a double-take. With the second glance he gasped, "Well, hello!"

Barnes made a cursory introduction and descended the three stairsteps.

"Sir, I wish we could stay," Cutty said looking straight at Claire. "But it's getting late and a storm's coming. We need to hop off this hump as soon as possible."

As the two soldiers turned to leave, Claire called down, "Adam, you're still my favorite dancing partner."

When Barnes reached that first knoll, he gracefully veered around. Claire was still standing on the porch watching his departure. Barnes struck a dancing pose; arm extended, and made one pirouette causing his helmet to spin loose. Recovering his balance and his liner, he stood erect and disappeared over the crest of the hill with a waving salute of his hand high in the air.

CHAPTER 21

TROPHIES FOR
TRUE CHAMPIONS

Every general medical officer soon learned upon arriving in Vietnam that they had two terms of duty within one tour—one in a forward field position and one in the rear area so to speak. Six months of one and a half-dozen for the other. Adjustments were easier if a doctor started out in a battalion-level field assignment and gradually eased back to a more civilian-style practice of medicine, e.g., an evacuation hospital or clearing company with a rear-echelon unit. Those docs who experienced the reverse (rear-to-field) had the more difficult adjustment.

Barnes had arrived in country expecting the worst placement because of his limited training. When he was designated a battalion surgeon, a position farther-most out on the army's medical chain, his inner attitude was already prepared. Now the new commission to the clearing company represented his first steps on the journey back to the real world and civilization.

A clearing company was staffed with three physicians: usually an internal medicine specialist, a general surgeon, and a general medical officer. The first two had achieved board certification in their fields, whereas the general medical officer probably just had the doctor of medicine degree at this point in his career. Adam Barnes was in this latter category—jack-of-all-trades, master of none.

Captain Jim Johnson, the internist, had been trained at Temple and Jefferson medical schools in Philadelphia, while the surgeon, Captain Will Wright, had done all his training at Medical College of Virginia in Richmond. Both men had seniority on Barnes in both age and time of service. They exuded confidence in the practice of army medicine, unflappable in demeanor. Nothing seemed capable of throwing them off their game. Barnes believed it had something to do with a "short-timers" threshold. They had passed the point of no return. In three months both would be hearing the double shouts of DEROS day.

The clearing company functioned a lot like an emergency room and resembled the MASH units of the Korean War. The days would vary with regard to number of cases and their critical urgency since most serious injuries and wounds would just be stabilized and transported to EVAC hospitals immediately, if they were brought in to the clearing company at all. MEDEVAC had transformed medical treatment in this war.

Captain Barnes kept mostly clinic hours with rotations every third day for emergency triage and treatment of the 15th Med Battalion personal health needs. The duty was not as enjoyable as the MEDCAP clinics, but thankfully slow—a positive sign of change for the indigenous community in and around Phuoc Vinh.

For Barnes this was to be the healthiest year of his life. Plagued by multiple allergies in the States, Adam remarkably became sick only once while overseas—a half-day bout of stomach flu from a pediatric contact. However, the primary danger to being exposed to the endemic population was not necessarily the people, it was their food. Partaking of the local cuisine could be and often was hazardous to the uninitiated's health.

Doctors made it a point to avoid sampling native fare, but in this new assignment, the outreach process advocated that the officers attend festivals and community activities in the region. Raw and undercooked dishes would be the foodstuffs of such outings, and American officers were instructed not to offend their Vietnamese hosts by refusing to partake of their gracious gifts of food. The CAV was making great progress in the villages, earning trust and confidence by their ability to provide security, especially in the daylight hours with a steady improvement during the night. First Team personnel were strongly encouraged not to upset the trust truce and thus jeopardize the public relations inroads being made locally.

Captain Barnes' good health record seemed at risk when he was instructed to attend a hamlet religious festival. He would have to eat the food offered to him or hazard offending the Vietnamese Council and village mayor. The event was in one of the MEDCAP villages where Barnes had done numerous pediatric "drop-ins."

Seated at the makeshift tables aligned in the village square, CAV dignitaries and city leaders sat awaiting the food platters to be served. It was early evening. In the recreational area of a nearby park, often frequented by soldiers playing basketball, a single explosion was heard. A ball had been left on the ground near the goal. Apparently, a child had wandered by, noted it lying there and inadvertently picked it up to play with it.

"Boom!" The blast ripped open the air. With horrifying consequences terrorism had struck an innocent bystander again.

The basketball had been booby trapped with a pressure-release explosive device beneath the ball, probably an old mine or fragmentation grenade. The thrust of the detonation had been aimed toward the court; since the child was passing on the periphery, only his hand was impacted by the flash.

The U.S. liaison officer for the public gathering quickly fetched Doctor Barnes. A T-shirt was wrapped around a child's tiny hand. Barnes thought to himself, "I know this kid!" In fact, he did. It was the candy bag boy from the MEDCAP clinic. The one who had fallen down, tripping over his baggy boxer shorts. It was months ago but Barnes remembered because of the laughable circumstances. Nevertheless, nothing funny existed about this situation. A tragedy is not a comedy in Barnes' mind—ever!

The doctor's heart was touched with dual emotions—angry passion and caring compassion. The lad was trembling. Yet the shaking was not from temperature, fever or cold; it was from fear. He was terrified and in shock.

Doctor Barnes swept the boy up into his arms, embracing him and his wrapped hand tightly. Barnes' driver arrived with a jeep and away they sped to the aid station.

In minutes the jeep pulled up beside the corrugated steel Quonset hut which housed the triage and treatment room of 15th Medical Battalion. The T-shirt pressure wrap was not overly soaked with blood. When he removed the cloth dressing, Barnes could see that the little finger of the boy's left hand had been severed at the metacarpal joint. The initial flare-burst had cauterized the site to some extent, thus the reduced bleeding. Many of the tendons in the palm were exposed and the skin tissue below the evulsion joint was charred and webbed. The wound would need extensive debriding and repair.

162

At first glance the hand looked unreal, like the crafted skeleton of an actor grotesquely made up for a horror movie. The physician's mind raced. Would this hand function normally again with all its muscular majesty? Hold a utensil, catch a ball, grip a bat... paint a picture? It would take a miracle. Just then it dawned on Adam where one might be found even in a war zone.

With the situation stabilized, Doctor Barnes decided to air ambulance the child to the 24th Evacuation Hospital. He was aware from some other referrals that an orthopedist who studied under Lenox Baker and John Goldman at Duke was there. (Doctor Goldman had been designated "the hand doctor" because of his amazing technical skill in reconstructive surgery of the hand.) The specialist at 24th Evac had played college football at Duke before going on to medical school and residency training in orthopedics there. His name was Billy Waddell.

"Waddell could do it!" Barnes thought excitedly.

Within an hour of this horrendous trauma, the child, with his mother and an interpreter, were airborne and on their way to Saigon. Barnes had seen to it that this little Vietnamese boy's *hand* was now *in the best hands* for wonder working care. With liftoff, Adam prayed.

In war, Adam Barnes understood that collateral damage to innocent victims was a reality but should never be accepted as the deliberate design. Those who intentionally targeted non-combatants for the sake of some sick political policy or propaganda would be forever condemned by Barnes for the cowardly act such behavior exhibited. A civilized society did not and should never specifically designate the innocent as the primary object of attack in war and should never condone such a strategy as a form of freedom fighting. Barnes would go one step further in advocating that every international body of governance in the world, United Nations and the like, should be vehement in their categorical condemnation of the inhumane practice of terrorism to intimidate and subjugate, to coerce and conquer, other human beings.

The pacification process was enhanced by rural village happenings which brought the American and Vietnamese cultures into proximity. By providing a more secure environment for local communities and exhibiting a genuine compassion for the people in incidents such as with the injured toddler, some hearts and minds were turning. Local leaders now construed the presence of the First Cav as an instrument of good, not one of evil. The previous and ongoing terror tactics of the Viet Cong factored into a growing alienation from the insurgents by the provincial population. In truth, an increasing number of local Cong members were defecting to the ARVN side. The Chieu Hoi program of repatriation to the South was experiencing some trickle down effect and after Tet, the flow of repates was steadily increasing.

The effectiveness of the First Cav surge into III Corps evidenced itself in the reduced numbers of rocket and mortar attacks on the cities and towns; in some areas, sporadic at best. Barnes recalled two of these sporadic attacks as notable while serving with 15th Medical Battalion.

As was his habit to be in chapel every Sunday, Adam continued the practice while at clearing company. On one Sabbath morning, the enemy chose to bring the chaplain's service to a screeching halt. Just as the benediction was about to be pronounced, several rocket launches could be heard in the distance. Whoosh,

whoosh, whoosh! There was a prayerful silence in the chapel, a primarily wood structure constructed upon foundational brick walls rising about two feet above the ground.

When the whop and whump of impact came into the compound, Barnes instantly rolled from his pew and embedded himself against the wall. Once again this was no place or time to be standing tall. As the shrapnel passed through and the incoming rounds passed on, Barnes was glad his faith had brought him to that place at that exact time. Just as with the three little pigs, bricks worked better than sticks and straw as a shield against flying shell fragments.

On another occasion the evening movie was being shown outside about half a click (mile) from the Phuoc Vinh airstrip. The cinematic presentation for the evening was *The Good, The Bad, And The Ugly* with Clint Eastwood and Eli Wallach. This tale of the Civil War was progressing along like most spaghetti westerns when the sound of incoming mortars came whistling down on the very position where Barnes and his colleagues were seated. Lawn chairs went launching in every direction as dozens of soldiers hit the ground. The projector just hummed along. After an awkward period of real-life "freeze frame," the source of the sounds was deciphered to be the Civil War battle scene of the movie, not an attack on the airfield. Nervous laughter was the usual sequel to such an act of embarrassment.

However, from Barnes' perspective it was always safer to drop since just three weeks earlier in the same location, the outside-theater, rounds of mortar fire came walking across the runway and down the jeep path between the barracks. Barnes was lying in such a position that he could view each exploding step as the rounds impacted closer and closer. One cannot imagine the sphincter tension-index that increases with every approaching blast. Fortunately, that time, the evening "walk" ended fifty yards from what would have been multiple injuries to numerous personnel of the 15th Medical Battalion. Contrary to popular opinion, no one was interested in receiving a Purple Heart Award if they could help it.

Regarding military awards, Captain Barnes received the Bronze Star while in his words, "just doing his job" at 1st/30th, and he was awarded the Air Medal for just flying in a helicopter back and forth to nine different LZs, during his first six months in the war. Now if one wanted to hear about a worthily decorated doctor, Barnes would tell you about another battalion surgeon who served with the CAV.

Captain Mark Moore was with the 7th Cav. His unit was in a firefight with the Viet Cong near Tay Ninh, an area known as "Rocket Alley." It was another tunnel-infested region where "gooks" would pop out of the ground, fire a rocket or rifle, then disappear deep underground before the ordinance could reach its target. These nests were hard to take out from the air.

On this day, a company of the 7th Cav was ambushed in an open field. The unit retreated to the tree line to the east while the enemy was entrenched to the west—no-man's-land was in the middle. With the initial skirmish, the infantry lieutenant was wounded and isolated in the open field. Viet Cong were popping up out of camouflaged spider holes all along the field and no American soldier could safely reach the fallen leader.

Field radio communications were being monitored by the lieutenant colonel commander of 7th Cav who was flying above the fray. The commander informed the ground troops that the doc was with him in the helicopter and could the battalion surgeon be of any help on the ground. The reply came quickly.

"Yes! Lieutenant Davidson is lying in the field and the medic says there is blood spurting out of his stomach."

The command Huey landed to the east behind some trees and Doctor Moore leaped out. The chopper immediately spiraled off to provide air support.

The medic was correct; binoculars revealed the telltale spurting of an abdominal arterial bleed. The young soldier would not live long under those circumstances. Moore asked for a "shoelace" and began to crawl out into the field behind a barrage of covering fire from M16s on the ground and M50s in the air.

When Moore reached the lieutenant, he observed that the right renal artery was lacerated. Deftly sliding the shoelace beneath and around the artery where it branches from the abdominal aorta, he tied it off. Then as the AK-47 fire decreased from the enemy side, he dragged the wounded soldier in the tandem fashion, both men sliding on their backs a foot at a time, until they were in the safety of the tree line—the company lieutenant's life was saved.

The intriguing aspect of the story came when this incident was written up for awards. At first, the lieutenant colonel was put in for the Silver Star with Oak Leaf Cluster for bravery and the physician was recommended for the Bronze Star with Oak Leaf Cluster (a lesser award). Interestingly, when the written accounts of this battle incident came across the awards desk at division headquarters, the reviewer noted the separately submitted reports were about the same encounter. The Board of Review changed the awards to what truly fit the facts. Doctor Moore was awarded the more elevated Distinguished Service Cross (which is just below the Medal of Honor) and the battalion commander had his citation request lowered to a Bronze Star with Cluster. Barnes would have concurred. Sometimes the army did get things right about who should be awarded the title of true champion.

However, in another situation involving one of Barnes' buddies from Fort Sam, the end turned out differently. Doctor Bob Smith (night map course "ankle sprain") was serving in a clearing company clinic near Saigon when a general came to it and tried to pull rank for the treatment of the common cold. The basic training friend of Barnes was busily treating several more serious situations in the clinic so Captain Smith informed the aide-de-camp that the general would have to wait.

On the one hand, the truth of the matter is that a captain physician represents the ranking authority in any army medical facility, even over a general. On the other hand, when the captain resumes his prescribed chain of command outside of medical duty responsibilities, the general rules. One week later, Barnes' former colleague found himself assigned as a battalion surgeon in the Mekong Delta swamps.

Barnes respected his buddy greatly for making that principled stand in spite of the potential for vindictive consequences. To Barnes, Bob Smith best exemplified a champion for the common soldier fighting in Vietnam.

Using the *Merriam-Webster Dictionary*, Barnes would nuance his definition of champion in three ways: a valiant fighter on the field of battle (Doctor Moore), a protector who fights on behalf of another for a principle (Doctor Smith), and a first-place winner in any competitive endeavor (Doctor Barnes).

The U.S. soldier historically could be affiliated with elements of all three of these definitive statements—being brave, undefeated fighters for the cause of freedom around the world...
true champions!

CHAPTER 22

ROUNDBALL AND OTHER RIVALRIES RESUME

Playing basketball in canvas combat boots rather than canvas Converse shoes afforded a unique challenge, physically and optically, considering the conditions of the outdoor courts. The boot kicked-up sprays of clay dust mixed in midair with the copter wash of powdery particles of dirt could easily become a visual barrier between the shooter and the goal. When the air was swirling around, taking outside shots demanded a lower trajectory in order to reach the rim and not be blown off course. Shooting long high-arching shots with basketballs was an adventure.

When Adam Barnes came over to 15th Med, the clearing company competitions in basketball between the officers and the enlisted men resumed where they had left off five months before—five-on-five, three-on-three, even two-on-two. When it was suggested by the officers that the sides be mixed, the NCOs refused, preferring the standard separations. For some, it was a cultural thing; for others, it was a competitive thing. The after-dinner games had surpassed engendering camaraderie and had advanced to the intensification stage of serious rivalry.

Over a two-month period, the officers remained undefeated

with Barnes playing for them—a streak which began that first night near the DMZ. The officers would have been comfortable with a loss, but the rabid determination of the enlisted players to win provided a strong motivation for the officers never to let them. The maturity of the officers would permit a loss with which to live, but no one wanted to lose. The goal was to go undefeated. The UCLA collegiate team was doing it back home so why not in Vietnam? That was the challenge. To stay undefeated in these games embodied Adam's personal goal. His opponents had made it a gauntlet rivalry and therefore one that he was determined never to lose. Never to give the enlisted men the satisfaction of beating the officers—for the latter, it was a game; for the former, a war.

The rivalry in the Vietnam saga was another story. It might appear that the United States was playing for a tie. Clearly, the game had changed after the crushing *military* defeat of the Communists during Tet. It had become a political and propaganda game. On the battle playing field the forces had won more and more decisive games in a season than the enemy. In truth, the USA team was still undefeated. However, at the level of politicians and world diplomats, an indecisive truce was being negotiated out of a stalemate. In fact, troop withdrawals back to the USA had already begun with the 9th Infantry Division. Players were being pulled off the field.

The enemy wanted to extend the game into overtime—over and over and over again. On the other hand, the allied team was already playing the game at a disadvantage with a handicapped and holding back kind of strategy.

Captain Barnes remembered the defiant words of that NVA regular who had been captured. In a bunkered aid station Barnes had been present to hear the soldier from a stretcher avow in Vietnamese, later translated for the doctor into English, "Your own people will make you come home!"

The intelligence found on the bodies of killed NVA coming out of Cambodia revealed that this was more than a dying man's statement. This was the game plan for the Northern invaders: "As the Ninth Division withdraws its forces, you are commanded to carry out more aggressive guerrilla warfare with the goal of maiming and killing as many of the U.S. soldiers as you can. This will give the impression that we have driven them out."

The concept of a moral victory by a defeated team is usually meaningless to the true competitive athlete; but as a propaganda tool in war, it can be devastating to those back home—a mother, a wife, an impressionable student. "Fight on, for their own people will make them quit."

Using a football analogy, one officer put it this way to Barnes. "It's like winning the game; and after the winning team leaves the field of play for the locker room, the opposing team retakes the field to score on the marching band." Such a scenario was troubling to most of the officers with whom Barnes was associated, though it was rarely articulated publicly with so blunt a pessimism.

Obvious to the First Cav, a counterattack by the enemy out of Cambodia was boldly developing in the west. In the North, Hanoi was preparing for an extended overtime period based on the wartime prolongation which protesting American politicians and students were providing. The game was over but those in the stands were not unified in accepting the military victory. The more vociferous demonstrators, by their premature preening prattle, were causing the First Team to be taken out of the game before the substitutes were prepared to play the opponent regulars in the overtime.

This endangering build-up revealed itself to the personnel at 15th Med when a LRRP squad had to be extracted under duress from Cambodia. This four-man team became exposed and entrapped behind the enemy lines. In the ensuing firefight, one member was killed and another wounded. The 15th Med was the nearest medical outpost. (All that Captain Barnes knew about LRRP units was that they had great instant meals. "LRRP rations, just add water to the bag and, voila, instant beef stroganoff.") These special-ops recon guys were selected from an unusual breed of men—high strung, hyperactive, close-knit, intense warriors. They lived alone, totally dependent on each other—back-to-back, side to side, a single functioning force.

One of their quartet had been killed. The manic behavior of the remaining three was off the chart. Adrenaline flowing and wild-eyed, they burst into the trauma section of the aid station. Frantically discarding gear and assisting the movement of a still alive but seriously wounded companion, they hovered anxiously like pacing parents would oversee the care of a child in the ER after a traumatic accident. Soon the ranger was stabilized—bleeding controlled, fluids and blood administered, pain medication provided. He received temporary treatment and then was whisked to an awaiting MEDEVAC helicopter for the brief trip to Long Binh and surgery.

As the helicopter lifted away, rumors were flying among the medics that a NVA prisoner had been thrown out of the rescuing chopper which had brought in the LRRP team. One could only imagine what might have transpired 200 feet above 15th Med's tarmac pad. The rage in the facial expressions of these young men said it all; an eye for an eye—a life for a life. This is not a game. *This is war!*

The remaining two rangers seemed to be gearing down as Doctor Barnes ministered to some minor shrapnel wounds and inquired about any other health issues before the two left for debriefing. Their conversations with each other, cot to cot as the medics carried out the doctor's orders sounded like a rehearsal recounting of what would be reported.

Apparently the team had been in Cambodia and had stumbled onto a spider hole entrance to a huge maze of subterranean tunnels. With a bent-angle flashlight in one hand and a .45-caliber pistol in the other, the patrol leader entered the hole. He found an empty residence chamber at the end of the first section with a trap door down to a second hospital level. Adeptly, the ranger had avoided the pit viper hung upside down in the first entrance.

(The Cong loved to use snakes as sentinels in their tunnels. They would force the reptile to swallow an indigestible marble or metal ball bearing about the size of a small egg. The object would create an anchor bulge along the length of the viper's body so a piece of hemp cord could firmly attach the snake's tail to a bamboo rod. The pole would be wedged into the tunnel walls overhead near the entrance. The pit viper would wrap around the pole. As a booby trap the serpent would wait in the shadows for some unsuspecting tunnel rat to slide beneath it at which point it would strike with its deadly poisonous fangs.)

When the spelunking specialist dropped down through the second trap door, he triggered some sort of alarm. The anthill came to life. He made it back out but had been bitten by the suspended viper in the face as he scrambled up the tunnel to the exit. A sentry sniper shot him in the back as he emerged from the hole. He was a dead man because of the snakebite; the sniper just hastened the inevitable end.

The LRRP report would provide valuable intelligence to S-2 but at what cost? The life of a leader and friend. The three who survived would be changed forever. Barnes wondered if such battle buddies could ever be acclimated back to civil society. The loneliness and daily living on the edge of danger would translate poorly in the pace of a civilized world. These men had provided their American comrades in arms an invaluable service—a warning about what was coming, what storm was gathering, and which elements of force would soon be unleashed upon them. It was a warning never to underestimate one's opponent. Vigilance was paramount. Forewarned is to be forearmed as the saying goes, and the First Team would take this foresight and plan the ultimate strategy for a second victory.

Considering the coming years, Adam Barnes questioned whether South Vietnam would be able to hold the full length and breadth below the DMZ, yet the geography of the ancient French colony of Cochin China, in all probability, could be cordoned off by those who had an impassioned desire for freedom. If not deserted by other freedom-loving countries, the South could survive. All they needed was time and training. Barnes believed in "Vietnamization" of the ARVN army to assume more of the burden of their country's defense. He envisioned a wall that could hold the Northern enemy out while the South prepared within to take responsibility for the future of their country. That was his ideal scenario, emphasis on "ideal."

The dream of a new and free nation seemed within an out-stretched reach from the shoulders of Nui Ba Dinh. The Montagnard people were so self-sufficient, subsisting for years above the war. It would appear that mountaineers were always free whether in the majestic hills of West Virginia or on the isolated mountain humps of South Vietnam.

While assigned to 15th Med, Doctor Barnes took advantage of the MEDCAP program continuing to hold pediatric clinics regularly at the Shepherd of The Hills orphanage. The visits had a mutual benefit. The children got to see a doctor and that doctor got to see their missionary nurse.

On the trips when Captain Barnes could spend the night on the mount with his old artillery unit, he and Claire would spend the early hours of the evening gazing at the heavens above while the war was waxing and waning below on the fertile plains, in the rice paddies, and across the neighboring rubber plantations. It was a time to talk and occasionally, even a chance to dance a Highland Fling.

During these rare excursions, Claire educated Barnes concerning the ways of the Montagnard people. How, as isolated bands of Vietnamese highlanders, they had proven to be exceptionally resilient in their adjustment to the many misfortunes of war. Trusting upon their own devices, creativity, and instincts, they always survived occupation and oppression. Being *left alone* and being *free* seemed to integrate these two qualities which mountaineers desired the most.

Unbeknownst to Adam Barnes, he would soon encounter one of these mountain men who had ventured down from the high land and found himself not above the fray but now buried deep with in it—***the war.***

CHAPTER 23

MINOR SURGERY ON A MAJOR

C hoosing to switch sides in a major sport rivalry would be rare, if not unheard of, in the States—athletic anathema, capricious, traitorous. But since Vietnam was *not a game,* such a switch could happen in a *war*—under certain consequential circumstances. Viet Cong fighters who surrendered or were captured could be repatriated into the ARVN army of the South if they elected to do so. The program was named "Chieu Hoi." It offered amnesty and rehabilitation to guerrillas who desired to defect. Special fighting units were constituted primarily with these defectors. They could be very effective against the insurgent soldiery since they were familiar with the communist enemy's tactics. Under guarded scrutiny by the U.S. Army, these soldiers were trained within the First Air Cav compound at Phuoc Vinh. American advisers were always cognizant of the possibility that these ex-Cong might revert to their old loyalties and turn terrorist again. However, if the rehabilitation process worked, these former adversaries could become ardent allies, an additional armed force for defense with which to be reckoned by the North Vietnamese regulars.

Since the re-orientation enclosure was located within the base perimeter, a Chieu Hoi trainee might be brought over to the clearing company clinic for routine medical treatment. American health care would be considered an unexpected perquisite of amnesty by these former guerrillas. Medical support for Vietcong raiders was hard to come by while they were on the move in the jungle.

It was late one Friday evening just past 2200 hours when the duty medic knocked on the screen door of Captain Barnes' hooch (residence quarters). Up to that moment the aid station had been quiet for the physician on call. Will Wright, general surgeon, was out of country on R&R in Hawaii with his wife and Internist Johnson had just DEROSed out, leaving Barnes the only available doctor at 15th Med. The heat and sticky humidity were high that night so Barnes was stripped down to wearing a T-shirt and undershorts. He slipped into his boots leaving them unlaced. The medic reported an emergency in the triage tank.

As the two men clogged over to the adjacent Quonset unit, the messenger gave Barnes a brief description of the situation. Jogging briskly created the only breeze in the still night air. The corrugated shell was dimly lit while the domed ceiling space was all in shadows. At the end of a row of cots sat a Vietnamese man on the examining table. His whole body was spotlighted by an overhead surgical lamp. He wore only black pajama bottoms which were soaked from the stream of blood running down his chest.

Apparently a brawl had broken out at the Chieu Hoi program barracks and one of the newest arrivals had been seriously injured. In the melee he had been struck with the edge of a trenching shovel, breaking his nose and savagely lacerating his face from the right nostril down into the upper lip. The wound was deep, incising through the gum to the bone and front teeth.

Skin, mucus membrane, and the circular layers of muscle about the mouth were involved. No fresh bleeding sockets in the gums indicating sites of forcibly knocked-out teeth were noted; however, the man had multiple toothless gaps from earlier dental losses.

Bleeding from the superficial cut was soon controlled by pressure pads and gauze sponges but the man was gagging because of the profuse postnasal drainage of blood. He was drowning and Barnes was praying that he would not have to do an emergency tracheostomy. Silently, Barnes flashed a prayer, "Lord please help me…TIBIA."

Using a curved hemostat, Barnes remolded the deformed septum and nasal bone to improve the airway, thus allowing the man to catch his breath, if only temporarily. Next, he pinched the nose and pressed his index finger hard along the pressure points above the upper lip. The bleeding slowed but continued. He then tried cotton swabs saturated with an epinephrine solution, but all these measures were not effective in reducing the oozing flow of blood. "Lord, Please…TIBIA."

A book! A book Barnes had lugged all over the countryside came to mind, *Fundamental Skills In Surgery*. He remembered an illustration on a page in the book. It was a lateral view of a sectional nasal cavity. It described the technique of packing a traumatized nose to control posterior bleeding.

The book was in his duffle bag in his quarters; the patient was in the ER. Doctor Barnes was preoccupied with applying delicate, constant pressure with both hands. He sent the medic to retrieve the textbook, stat. The kid responded, "stat!"

"Look up injuries to the nose!" Barnes barked. Within seconds the illustrated page was found. Following the steps outlined in the book, the doctor made the necessary positioning of gauze in the back of the throat. He used forceps, lengths of suture material, and catheters to thread the lines through the nasal and oral passages. First the posterior and then anterior cavity was packed. The patient moved only his eyes to follow Barnes in every movement of the doctor's head. Barnes read, then worked while reading over his shoulder. Back to the face, back to the book, back to the nose—reading, placing, adjusting, and reading again.

After gently pulling on the strings and securing the ribbony folds of gauze in each nostril, Barnes noted that the bleeding had stopped. It was a strange sight to see strings like spaghetti hanging out of the man's mouth and both nostrils, but the pack was working.

Now came the hard part—how to close the facial laceration so that the mouth would be functional and somewhat cosmetic in appearance. Barnes had very little hands-on surgery experience. However, he had assisted on the repair of a cleft palate for an infant during his internship. What he had observed was how important it was to get all the right layers in apposition during closure—muscle to muscle, mucosa to mucosa, margins matching margins.

In this case the laceration, though deep, had sharp, clean edges. A few raw, jagged ones were debrided quickly for a more satisfactory closure. Barnes detected that the xylocaine field block was beginning to wear off based on some facial muscular twitching. Not a sound or moan was uttered from this stoic soldier, a diminutive warrior of around five feet tall. The twitch alone was telling Barnes that he would have to speed up his repair. Infiltrating to numb and thus distorting the skin lines more would be a problem. He hoped his patient could take the pain. First the muscle, then the other subcutaneous soft tissue, and finally the skin was sutured closed. A Barton figure-of-eight bandage was entwined around the head to immobilize the jaw. A redundant elastic band was fashioned over the Barton and was finished with multiple wraps around the neck to anchor it in place. The patient's head was close to resembling a mummy.

A sterile technique performed with gowns and gloves, though practiced some, had limited value in an environment swirling with contaminants. Every forward base and field surgery in Vietnam was covered with antibiotics. This case would be no different. Wonder-working penicillin was administered along with pain medication which had the effect of putting this man instantly to sleep.

Barnes was not that concerned about the bleeding now or the possibility of infection. He was apprehensive about the facial and jaw movements of a sleeping patient. He had tried to immobilize the head with ace bandages and the hands with wrist restraints. For all the above reasons and more, Barnes determined that the patient would not be returned to his compound but would stay in the officer's barracks while Captain Wright was away on R&R. There was an extra bed and Barnes could more easily check on his patient through the night.

It was way after midnight when the Vietnamese defector was transferred by stretcher to Barnes' private ward. A security guard was posted on duty outside. Initially Barnes remained awake to monitor any bleeding or breathing complications. He took hourly vital signs until 0500 hours. Eventually, fatigue won out and drowsiness overwhelmed him. The doctor nodded off to sleep.

At 0600 hours Barnes was startled from his doze to find the head bandages piled on the empty bed, and the Chieu Hoi patient sitting on the floor. He was attempting to remove the second hand restraint. His eyes were trained on Captain Barnes. The sutures were still in place and the knotted strings of the nasal pack were still protruding from the man's nose. Dark blood had begun to ooze slightly from the mouth—not seriously nor as severe as the night before.

After a tense few seconds the patient pointed to his lower jaw and mumbled, "dau…con dau," the Vietnamese words for pain.

Point tenderness was elicited upon examination by Barnes. In addition to a small fracture/tear to the bony upper palate, an x-ray revealed a hairline fracture on the right side of the jaw. The placement of the Barton wrap had exacerbated the point of pain at the break site, and this explained why the soldier had removed the bandages when the pain medication had worn off.

Barnes reasoned that the impetus of the attacking blow with the shovel was so forceful that the steel base of the adjustable handle bludgeoned the lower jaw. The man was fortunate that the fracture was not compound and that he did not lose any teeth. His assailant had not held back. This was a vicious attack. Why?

In the days which followed, some background information was acquired. The patient in actuality had recently been a major in the Vietcong. His name was Thieu Chai. He had commanded a company of insurgents in the hill country near Cu Chi. On the other hand, most of the other defectors in the prisoner program had been affiliated with guerrilla groups in the urban region of Saigon. They now had converted and become nationalists who opposed the reunification with North Vietnam and its associated communist oppression.

In the past, Major Thieu had sympathized with the Vietminh brand of communism against French colonialism. He had been impressed with the concepts of the community, as a whole, owning the property and then equally distributing the economic goods among the people. The Vietcong had demonstrated this form of social service as their initial approach to outreach. The communists used the language of unification and nationalism stressing independence and the establishment of democratic freedoms. Thieu had only heard about but never had seen the ruthless side of communism.

At the most vulnerable moment of his life, the emotional devastation associated with the death of his wife, Thieu joined the communist insurgency. Vengeance may have been a motivating force in the decision, but Thieu had been silent on the matter.

After the Tet Offensive failed to ignite the flames of revolution and Thieu was captured, he had time to contemplate the whole idea of reunification, personally and politically. By now he had observed the hidden, horrific side of communist exploitation of villages and the terror tactics applied when some hamlets refused to feed and shelter the Cong. Under the circumstances, Thieu Chai chose to enter the pacification process to survive and to serve in the Rural Development Program with the South Vietnamese. He would not be fighting but would be leading a cadre of servants.

Captain Barnes acknowledged the obvious rivalries of ideology and of rank and of national geography that existed between the Chieu Hoi soldiers, but none of these issues could explain the attack. That is until the interpreter made a reference to a racial slur. Barnes asked him what the term meant. From the "Terp's" explanation it became clear to Barnes that the possibility of racial prejudice may have played a role.

Major Thieu was a "half-breed." His father had been a Montagnard villager from the Central Highlands of Vietnam while

his mother was of French-Indochinese descent. The urban guerrillas of the South had little respect and a growing contempt for
the Montagnard people and their tribal isolationist views. By and
large the hill people had historically attempted to remain neutral in the recurrent political and civil strife of Indochina. They
were not sold out to becoming a communist "colony" much less
a democratic one. They just wanted to be left alone to practice
their ancient culture and live out their lives in peace and freedom.

Midmorning Captain Barnes sent for the CAV interpreter,
and after a brief interrogation concerning the altercation, the decision was made not to return Major Thieu to his compound. It
would be an unwise risk for him. Whatever had instigated the
first brutal assault still existed based on the Military Police report. A vow of silence among the Chieu Hoi trainees was hinder-
ing the investigation. Obviously the animosity of someone in the
Ex-Cong unit had been so intense that he or they had attempted
to kill the Montagnard Major. Why else would someone take a
shovel to a man's head while he slept?

Now the greater problem at hand for Dr. Barnes was how to
immobilize the patient's jaw to permit healing of the facial recon-
struction. Barnes was contemplating some kind of makeshift oc-
clusive bandaging method to stabilize the upper and lower jaws
together. He got on the land line phone to his UNC dentist buddy, Brian Jenner, who was stationed at Long Binh.

After some catch-up conversation, Captain Jenner guided
Barnes in performing the occlusion of the teeth rows using metal
wires. Direct bony wiring would require better facilities and better

skill than to which Barnes had immediate access. Therefore, the approach recommended was to attach wires around opposing sets of bicuspid teeth and then lock the jaw into occlusion by twist-ratcheting the wire ends. It took until that afternoon for the task to be completed.

Upon regaining consciousness since the patient had been sedated again, the ARVN interpreter explained the importance of allowing the facial incisions to heal. Food would have to be administered through a needle-less syringe for a short time and later a straw. The 15th Med army cooks tried to be creative with the various broth concoctions of pulverized vegetables. Yet a crushed-grain, watery rice soup (a Vietnamese staple) turned out to be the Chieu Hoi major's only accepted choice of nutrition.

For the first few days the only communication between Thieu and Barnes was through studied stares. If looks could kill, Barnes felt he should be dead. In time, the intensity of the glare-downs was reduced. The eyes softened somewhat, but the facial expressions of a former enemy were still dark and cold. Gradually recovery progressed to the point that the patient, *on the surface,* appeared to be accepting that he was getting better—thanks to the American doctor.

From other sources the Vietnamese interpreter had been able to piece together some more family history: Thieu's wife, caught in a crossfire battle between ARVN and Viet Cong troops, had tragically been killed—an event that catapulted Thieu into the war on the side of the Cong insurgents. His son, only two years old at the time of the accidental shooting, was taken to the orphanage at Nui Ba Dinh initially until the relatives of Thieu's father could adopt him. They lived in a small hamlet at the foothills near the mountain.

Major Thieu had been captured during the January Tet Offensive and was in the rehabilitation program training to become an ARVN officer. No one ever knew his true allegiance because he was a man of very few words, reserved and aloof in manner, cool in his carriage. He would lead by physical example more so than by verbal command. Since he was in this defector unit, it was assumed he was a "friendly," supportive of the South Vietnamese national movement—thus an American ally.

At the end of four days Thieu seemed to have recovered enough to have the nasal packing removed. At the end of the week the wires were extricated from his teeth. The laceration was healing nicely though a harelip scar he would bear for the rest of his life.

Will Wright returned from Hawaii a rejuvenated man; and within days of his return a new internist was assigned to 15th Med. Their presence meant the end of Barnes' running the officer's barracks like a rehab ward. Wright consulted on the status of Thieu and pronounced him fit to resume limited duty.

Barnes still was hesitant to release his patient back to the training compound and discussed the options with Wright while they sat on the front steps of the barracks. However, nothing would be able to override the authority of the ARVN command in this matter. Thieu was their soldier, not the Cav's.

In the end Barnes knew his patient had to be returned to the

Chieu Hoi Program. He would instruct the interpreter to tell Thieu in the morning about the transfer back.

However, before the lazy sun had illuminated the horizon of a new day, Thieu Chai's floor mat was empty. He had slipped out of the hooch during the night, slithered under the perimeter rings of barbed wire without detection, and was never to be seen again.

CHAPTER 24

TO TEACH OR NOT TO TEACH

Entering the final quarter of his year of days, Adam Barnes was presented with a choice for a new challenge. Phuoc Vinh had been his home base for nine months and now a return to the starting point at Bien Hoa was an unexpected possibility.

When the First Air Cavalry made the move from the DMZ to III Corps, the division general headquarters was established at Bien Hoa to the east of the U.S. Air Base. In fact, it was right beyond the end of the air strip runways themselves. The Cav's administration operations embodied a two-thousand member support staff, but only one physician for medical care.

Captain Tom O'Neal was in his DEROS month, and his replacement was being sought. Two general medical officers would soon be required to man this rear aid station since the medical mission was to be expanded. A new-arrival training camp would soon be attached to the support unit of administration. In addition to medical exams and health record reviews of incoming replacement soldiers, the doctor would be responsible for the personal hygiene and preventive medicine lectures along with weekly drug orientation seminars. The program brass were

189

looking for a good communicator who could design and deliver these training talks as a part of the orientation curriculum.

Since the clearing company routine did not provide time for MEDCAPS into the nearby villages and trips to Nui Ba Dinh had been curtailed, Barnes reasoned that Bien Hoa would be a good setting for him. It would advance him in the right direction on the DEROS game board—moving him multiple spaces back from the field and closer to passing go in route to home. Moreover, the U.S. Air Base had to be one of the safest places in all of Vietnam, it would seem to him. He was a short-timer with nothing to prove. Since he had paid his field dues, he accepted the new duty assignment.

Barnes believed that his store of practical knowledge gleaned from the field might help some incoming newbie, hearing it from a war-doc who was familiar with the front. A route-stepping officer empathetic with the new-in-country-soldier and his up-country plight—a comrade who understood fear and who expressed gratitude for a soldier's service to his native nation. However, the American home front had been drastically changing since Barnes left its shores.

———————

Across the ocean, emanating more loudly from the left coast came a deluge of devastating disdain for the war and its U.S. military participants. The new breed of draftee and recruit had been infected by invective, besieged, besmeared, and besmirched in character. They had experienced firsthand the hateful stares, the spiteful spitting, and the thoughtless taunts of "baby killer." Motivating these teens and young adults was becoming a hard task, and an even harder sell. The mission of *fighting to set men free* from Communist oppression and totalitarian tyranny was being diluted of its honor. What is right and pure was being distilled out, leaving a distillate of disgrace in Congress and on the college campuses. At least that was how the transformed mind of Adam Barnes envisioned it. The lines between the good, the bad, and the evil were being blurred in multiple media sources, and the young American soldier was being asked to drink the dregs being served up across the counter-culture of illicit drugs and anti-war protests.

Before captive audiences of new cavalrymen conditioned by politicized propaganda back home stood Captain Adam Barnes. As a born-teacher he would attempt to counter the counter-culture. The orientation lectures he gave were serious but fun with lots of laughter and humor. His public speaking skills allowed him to tell stories rather than just address the troops with platitudes and clichés. He could keep the attention of 300 men, even in the sweltering afternoon heat. His standup presentation was not a look-to-the-right and look-to-the-left style lecture. He told it like it was with women and with drugs and how distractions associated with both could get a buddy killed in the field. He had the freedom to teach truths—even subtle biblical ones ("do unto others . . . more blessed to give . . . the strength of a threefold cord")—truths that could save a life or at least prevent physical misery in the field.

Barnes stressed the value of the *team,* not the lone individual. The trained ability to focus 24-7 was crucial to survival once a soldier left the safe confines of the training facility. Combat conditioning coupled with the ability to concentrate would assure a confidence on the field of battle. The principle of the weakest link was hammered home by Barnes and could not be emphasized enough.

The daily medical record reviews were tedious, but O'Neal and Barnes usually only had to handle the controversial ones. The station medics and tech specialists were excellent in screening the malingerers. Barnes encountered one gung ho, John Wayne type who arrived ready to take on "Charlie." Within two days he was back at the dispensary having gotten tangled up in the rappelling rope off the tower. The physical exam revealed a possible torn cartilage of his right knee. Barnes referred him to Long Binh for an orthopedic consult.

Two days passed and then he returned to be discharged medically back to the states for surgery. His war was over and his thanks to Barnes for making the disqualifying diagnosis was profuse. Very few men really have a zeal to kill. Most of the bravado types whom Barnes encountered were more bark than bite—more talk and less fight. For the most part, soldiers in the field respected that Vietnam was *not a game. It was a war!*

On another occasion a new arrival presented with the chief complaint of shin splints. Barnes was aware of this condition, most common in runners of track. The rookie had described the condition precisely but at the present he did not exhibit any visible symptoms. All Barnes could counsel him to do was go on to his assigned duty station in the field, but he was encouraged to check in with his battalion surgeon immediately on arrival at his new unit, sharing his medical history with the doctor in advance. Then, at the first attack of inflammation and swelling, he was to report for sick call and have the case confirmed by his medic. After the young grunt's first flare up, he too returned to the rear for transfer back to the States. His waging of a walking war was over and he was appreciative of the sympathetic advice from Captain Barnes.

The issue of a war zone physician having to do what some stateside, screening doctor should have done incensed Barnes. Some days it just exasperated him; on others, it infuriated his every fiber. The passion of anger was rising. "Be angry but sin not" was a recurring biblical thought.

The most ridiculous situation encountered was the regular army sergeant who had been passed on by every medical officer in the chain of transfer from Germany, Fort Dix, Fort Hood, and Guam to Vietnam. He had some legitimate health concerns but was told at every stop to "bring it up to the medical doctor at your next duty station." There he sat before Barnes with a thick folder of medical records in hand. A brief scan of the hospitalizations alone revealed he was forty years old, a diabetic with one kidney, who suffered from hypertensive heart disease. Barnes was livid by the time he finished the initial diagnosis forms. Any physician along the review process could have put a hold on these orders if they had spent five minutes reading his chart. This patient had no business being anywhere near Southeast Asia, especially where the potential for dehydration was so high. The old soldier was on the next freedom-bird flight back to the mainland stat. In his file was a very caustic note of inquiry for the medical officer of his next duty station: *What were they thinking declaring this man fit for duty in Vietnam?*

———————

Civilians back home can get war weary if the only media diet they receive is pound-into-the-ground pessimism sprinkled heavily with casualty figures and cost overruns. In such a negative climate, even those who are entrusted with the task of fighting the assigned battles can get war weary. Sarcastic humor and cynical folk hymns can permeate the atmosphere and undermine the aptitude and the appetite of a soldier to fight for the freedom of others.

Barnes kept replaying the words of that captured NVA soldier: "Your own people will cause you to quit and go home." The newbie soldiers coming over from the states were entering the country with doubts implanted from abroad. They exited the planes at Bien Hoa with questions swirling around in their brains. "Where was the enemy? Who was the enemy? Whose side are our Stateside countrymen on?"

Barnes could only recall how confused and alone these green, replacement sky troopers had to feel going from the "fickle" frying pan of home into the fixed fire of Vietnam.

As Barnes entered the aid station he noticed something was wrong. It was abuzz with activity, a rare occurrence this early in the morning. Back in his office sat a bird colonel from the 7th Cav; two MPs stood at the door guarding a seated soldier with handcuffs on his wrists. The officer was overseeing the expeditious discharge of this lowly private from the CAV back to the United States for court martial. Apparently on the previous evening this soldier had left a live grenade outside the quarters of the commanding general of 7th Cav. Such a deliberate act (later to be dubbed affectionately with the term "fragging") was not to be tolerated behavior in the field. The event set in motion the fastest evacuation of a soldier from the front lines that probably had ever happened, short of summary execution. In less than twenty-four hours this young man would be gone from the red clay soil of Vietnam, and within seventy-two hours he would be in a stateside prison cell awaiting court martial for attempted murder.

The role for Barnes in this discharging process was to give a medical exam, review the man's health records, and pass him down the line to admin for final disposition. In the back of his mind Barnes wondered, "Did this guy have anything against doctors?" It was clear he did not have much regard for authority figures like generals.

This was Adam Barnes' first encounter with a person who truly couldn't care less about whether he lived or died—whether he died alone or took other innocents with him. His background was Chicago, Illinois. A youth of the streets. The draft had brought him into the army. One could speculate about his upbringing, a fatherless, hard life for sure.

A dark, vacant stare projected from deep within his eyes. His responses were whispered, abrupt, and brief. A war was going on inside of him. He was a loner, deeply in emotional pain, a teen who had beaten up and been beaten up in the "hood." A lot of anger had brought him to this stage of "let's get it over with." No melodrama, only melancholia. This young man alone, in his despondent state, knew the why for his dastardly act of resentment.

Once his good physical health was confirmed professionally, that is, fit to be discharged, the former infantryman was whisked away in a "star-licensed" jeep—the colonel, the two MPs, and the lowly soldier of foreboding—and another day in the life of war went on.

Such were the day-to-days of Captain Barnes in Bien Hoa. But it was the nights that were even more frustrating. Drugs, drunks, and gang beatings were the emergency situations that filled the medical docket after 2200 hours. when the clubs would close. The number of frivolous complaints were causing Barnes to question whether he had made the right decision to accept this rear assignment. Though he enjoyed the teaching and the training talks, he doubted whether he was doing any medical good just sewing up knife wounds and babysitting the drug overdosers.

With O'Neal gone and no replacement, Barnes was the only doctor for two-thousand men. Being on call 24-7 was getting old. His energy was easily sapped by the daily confrontational conditions, having to prove constantly that someone was fit for duty rather than treating someone who was genuinely ill and in need of care. The thought that was crossing Barnes' mind with some frequency was "Put in for a transfer. Request to be sent back out to the field: the boonies, where there were young men who deserved to be helped medically."

After one exceptionally busy weekend call, Barnes was right on the verge of submitting for a transfer back to Phuoc Vinh and the camaraderie of 15th Med. He was torn between teaching the new guys how to stay healthy or treating the old guys who were battle weary and battle wounded.

Of the over five hundred thousand soldiers based in Vietnam, teenagers and young adults made up the bulk of the 20 percent who actually were fighting the war. Barnes had enormous respect for those young eighteen- and nineteen-year-old grunts humping in the Fishhook province and along the Cambodian border. They were worthy of the highest support their nation could supply— and they were not getting it.

CHAPTER 25

A LIFE PUT IN
UNCALLED-FOR JEOPARDY

A set of audio headphones earmuffed the scalp while rock-and-roll music coursed the wires from a second-hand, reel-to-reel tape player. Listening to music was a restful diversion for Barnes between the pseudo-emergencies of the evening. Any distraction of attention could be dangerous in Vietnam like a diversionary trick by the enemy in a war or a diversionary tactic by a rival in a game. Recorded music embodied neither of these two diversions while in the rear and out of the field of fire. Nevertheless, enjoying tunes was still a pleasant departure from the normal as Adam sat alone in his hooch at night. He trusted the medic in charge to summon him back to reality for any after-hours medical crisis. On the other hand, the aid station personnel were secretly entertained and laughably amused by the off-key vocalizations of their captain when he thought no one could hear him singing along with the tapes.

Adam Barnes mixed well with people. His manner was sociable and fun-loving *in the real world;* but he never wasted energy on being something he was not—someone he was not. He conserved his energy for being whom he was created to be.

However, *in the world of war* he consciously chose to live

somewhat aloof to stay alive. Adam exercised every effort *not* to get very close to anyone because it conjured up old fears of the impact of loss. Such a philosophy could be attributed to the consequences of war (people getting killed), but Barnes carried his reserve to extremes probably because of the death of his brother. Distance, detachment, and inaccessibility were defense mechanisms against personal pain and hurt. As he saw it, sentimental attachment threatened to distract a soldier from recognizing danger—for himself and for his men.

Therefore, as a self-imposed loner, what did he do for idle amusement? He was not a carouser. Drinking alcoholic beverages, taking drugs, and smoking cigarettes were not a part of his entertainment lifestyle. Ever since his college fraternity days his goal was to have fun without beer, pot, or nicotine. He could have a merry old time, remember it, and stay in control. Staying in control seemed to be a crucial aspect. In fact, unhealthy dissipations of any form did not seem to fit into his traditional belief structure. Barnes had settled on these prescriptions for himself while trying to avoid prescribing judgmentally for anyone else. However, it was hard to miss where Adam Barnes stood on an issue. All one had to do was ask. His credo was threefold: always tell the truth; always keep your promises; and always take full responsibility for the consequences of your conduct.

The consequences of bad behavior he strived hard to avoid. Out of control conduct he condemned, for others and for himself. In his mind self-denial was prerequisite to self-control. Although his constraint bordered on compulsion, he trained himself to bridle any excessive enthusiasm—no celebratory gestures, shouts, or dances on the field of play. It could be said accurately that when and while he competed in sports, he never heard the band.

Claire Marshall would confirm these staid traits observed in her camp friend. Barnes did not know how to let go. He was humbly inhibited to a fault. Still guarded, not yet free. Marshall's favorite descriptive term for Barnes was "stodgy," and she was *not* referring to a bulky physical build.

A demonstrative example of Barnes' inability to celebrate publicly came on the final day of February in 1964. It was the last basketball game of the regular season his senior year at Duke. By tradition, that game for years would be between the Blue Devils and the UNC Tar Heels. In that leap year the rivalry contest was scheduled for Woollen Gymnasium in Chapel Hill. Duke ended up whipping Carolina by the highest defeat differential in history: 104 to 69, a 35-point differential. In addition, it was the class of 1964's tenth straight win over UNC—four years undefeated in the rivalry was a record. Barnes had been the high point man for the game scoring twenty-eight points (a career best for him). And what did he do to celebrate that unprecedented streak on a Saturday night? While trees were toilet-papered across the quadrangles and parties were popping up all over Durham, he slipped silently off to the library.

As a pre-med student Barnes was advised that in order to get accepted into Duke Medical School he would have to take an advanced physics course—one which all the engineering school students were required to take. He had put it off until his senior year. After this biggest loss ever was handed to the Tar Heels on their home court, Adam Barnes was seen leaving his fraternity house for the quieter east campus library to study for a major test assigned for that next Monday. What a waste of a win his teammates and friends would deride. Years later overseas, another rivalry was being played out, yet *it was not a game. It was a war!*

So what did Barnes do for relaxation whenever he got some free time from the war? Certainly it was not the officer's club. Like Stonewall Jackson, who also neither smoked tobacco, drank alcoholic beverages, nor gambled in card games, both men, held Sundays as sacrosanct. (Historically, sometimes Jackson refused to march or fight on the Sabbath.) So what then for relaxation? In the field and in the rear the answer was the same—*sports*. Recreational sports and games had always been his release, his joy.

One afternoon on an excursion over to the air force library (a quality facility) on the opposite side of the Bien Hoa base, Barnes stumbled onto an indoor basketball court located in the ARVN special forces camp. This roofed, open-air pavilion for him became a great venue for physical exercise—jogging, shooting basketball, and practicing tae kwon do.

After the evening meal and before the evening sick call, Barnes would sneak off in the jeep around the end of the runway and into the special forces camp gate—one of the many points of entry attached to the airfield. All the air force facilities were on the southeast side while the First Cav Division area was on the northeast corner. It was a five-minute trip by vehicle.

Army Captain Barnes became a familiar face to the air force guards who manned the gate. He usually entered the ARVN compound in daylight hours, heading back just after dark. For the first few months, Barnes was never challenged upon entering the special forces camp. The canopied court/shelter was less than thirty feet inside the air force security guard post.

After the air force base command imposed a new, more rigid directive to tighten the restrictions around this particular gate, the army was not notified. The consequences of this crackdown for any army personnel became quite complicated.

One evening Captain Barnes was following his usual routine. He had delivered his afternoon medical lecture (health, hygiene, sex, and drugs) to the new arrivals and had grabbed a quick bite at the officer's club grill without returning to the aid station. All he had with him in the jeep was his medical kit used in his lecture and a pair of gym shoes he had recently purchased. He arrived at the gate around 1800 hours and entered without incident. Nightfall was fast enveloping the base because of dark cloud cover.

On this particular occasion, Barnes had stayed longer in the camp having shot ball with a young ranger named John Edmonds. He was one of the training advisers assigned to this Vietnamese special OPS unit housed in the ARVN encampment.

When Barnes attempted to leave the compound en route to the army side of the airstrip in his jeep, he was stopped. The guard was new at his post and was carrying out his orders. He did not know Army Captain Barnes and so he called over his sergeant who had seen Barnes before. For some reason the air force was not allowing anyone through <u>that</u> gate after dark even if they had proper identification.

As Lt. Edmonds was passing by his workout area, he came over to vouch for Barnes, but still the airmen were unrelenting. It seemed to Barnes that this top sergeant was enjoying his power over the army officer. After the lieutenant verified Barnes' identity, a frustrated Barnes attempted to drive past the guards and through the open gate. The first airman jumped in front of the vehicle and refused to move, tapping his hand and rifle on the hood. The stalemate was now complete.

Edmonds, recognizing that he had no jurisdiction over the

air base security detachment, invited Barnes back to his billet. He would call the air force duty officer-in-charge. That person would have the authority to inform the guards to let Barnes pass.

Edmonds rang up the Bien Hoa base headquarters and eventually was put in touch with that evening's duty officer, a major "something." He didn't get his name because the landline was filled with unusual amounts of static. After affirming the identity of Barnes as a U.S. Army physician with the CAV, he handed the phone to Barnes. A detailed account of the situation was tactfully provided and permission to pass was requested.

After a succinct explanation of the restrictions linked to that particular ARVN entrance, the major acknowledged that he could not authorize Barnes to enter the base by that gate. The recent tightening of security from the ARVN camp into the base had been necessitated by intelligence reports. Yet Barnes was not an ARVN soldier, he was an American.

Fueled by his earlier encounter at the gate, the instant reaction by Barnes to this refusal was anger. He informed the major that he needed to be back at his clinic by 2000 hours. The major replied with the option. "Captain, you know you can enter the main south gate."

It was about a mile and a half around and outside the perimeter of the base.

Barnes sarcastically shot back ignoring protocol, "Sir, can you have one of your men loan me a weapon since I am unarmed?"

"No!"

"Sir, have you ever been out in the field?"

"What difference does that make, captain?"

"A lot of difference!"

And with that Barnes violently slammed the phone back into

its casing and stormed out to his jeep. He jumped in and headed for the ARVN village-side exit which led in the opposite direction out of the compound beyond the protective safekeeping of the air base. Barnes would have to travel weaponless for under two miles and through two Vietnamese hamlets in order to arrive at the main south gate of the American air base.

Barnes was hot; combustive hot, molten lava hot, on-fire hot. As mad as he was, if anyone had dared to fire a bullet at him, his angry aura would have melted the projectile before it even reached his body.

Along the dirt road puddled and pocked from rain, Barnes' vehicle sped with lights on only intermittently. "How could a U.S. soldier do that to a fellow officer?" he thought. "Where's the professional courtesy? Surely those guards could see that I was not an enemy threat. I'm six foot three, white, and speak English fluently. Tomorrow I'm going to track that major down, face-to-face. He *could* have made that decision. He *should* have made that decision."

Barnes slowed and turned off his headlights as he approached the first village. With his head cocked slightly to the left, accentuating his night vision focus to the peripheral right, he could still make out the basic structural details of shops and huts. The town was quiet; nothing was moving. He accelerated through. So far, so good, he felt, beginning to calm down. The second village was just around the next bend.

Again the jeep lights were extinguished and the speed initially decreased. Good thing. Out of the corner of his owl eye, Barnes picked up the outline of several obstacles in the roadway. Two carts were upended in the middle of his path and a moped bicycle lay to one side blocking the only avenue of bypassing t' obstructions. Two men in dark clothing stood up from behind the cart barriers. AK-47 rifles were slung over their shoulders. Another was kneeling beside a crumpled body. The fallen man was moving his head and arms. His clothing was light in color.

One of the pajama-clad men gestured with the barrel of his rifle for Barnes to get out. Defenseless, Barnes climbed out with his hands raised. His first assumption was that he now was a prisoner of war. A flashlight was aimed into his eyes, then beamed down upon his lapel and back to his face.

"Dai uy, bac si?" the armed Vietnamese male interrogated.

Barnes recognized the first word as meaning his rank of captain. But he could not distinctively decipher the second, repeated in an abrupt and harsh manner. The compelling tone of his capturer expressed urgency. With a threatening jab of the weapon, Barnes was ushered around the carts to an elderly looking man, though probably only fifty years of age. He could have been younger but it was hard to tell in the shadows. The old man was having difficulty breathing.

Barnes surmised that this cyclist had wrecked into the ambush barrier of carts while riding on the Honda in the dark. Barnes was physically forced down to exam the man.

"You help!" was the command.

The doctor's simple touch to the chest revealed air bubbles crackling under the skin. A cursory exam noted several ribs probably fractured, one compound break creating a sucking chest wound with a collapsed lung. The little man's heart was racing and the silhouette of his neck showed a shift in his trachea. Not a good sign. His respiratory distress was severe and sudden death was a distinct possibility. Timely medical care was of the essence.

The American doctor took charge instinctively, gesturing for a cart to be righted. Carefully they lifted the old man onto the flatbed surface, and the cart was backed under the lean-to roof of a nearby hut. The cart was positioned so the jeep headlights could provide illumination.

Barnes mentally fired off his flash prayer. "Lord, help, please... and TIBIA!" Two words came to mind: dog surgery. On the one hand, an offensive phrase for a dog lover like Barnes; yet on the other, a valuable reference point to the Medical Education for National Defense program at Duke. Surgical procedures were practiced in this training lab on how to cope with gunshot wounds to the chest. Barnes started shuffling through both the emergency first aid kit and his lecture box in the vehicle, while the patient faded into a semi-conscious state.

The compound fracture site provided an open entryway to the chests pleural cavity so Barnes took advantage of it. Clamping a piece of rubber tubing with forceps, Barnes thrust the tip into the makeshift "incision." In one move he dissected beneath the chest wall, up two ribs, and punctured through the pleural lining forcefully. Pop! Whoosh! The immediate release of pressurized air was heard. Now the trick was keeping outside air from being sucked back into the pleural space when the man inhaled.

To achieve this, Barnes fashioned a makeshift flutter valve out of a condom he used for demonstration in his lectures. After cutting off the top end section, he secured the unrolled condom to the end of the tubing with coils of suture tie. The confirmation that the "valve" was working came with the escaping air emitting a sound like humming across a wax-paper kazoo—coarsely vibrating and quavering.

Almost immediately the internal air expansion pressure was reduced and the man's trachea was shifting back to the midline.

Using a tube of bacitracin ointment like Vaseline, Barnes created an airtight compression pad with coated squares of gauze. He then bandaged the whole chest and taped the flutter tube down securely.

Just as Barnes placed the final strip of tape on the chest wrappings, a Vietnamese man in civilian pants and shirt was escorted into the shed. "Bac si, Bac si," they were acknowledging and pointing.

"I, too, doctor!" The civilian touched Barnes' Caduceus uniform patch. The unknown term that Barnes could not translate was in fact the Vietnamese word for doctor. Wearing the emblem with the snake wrapped around the winged staff probably had saved his life.

With the arrival of the provincial doctor the circumstances seemed to change. Barnes conveyed what he had done cautioning that the patient needed to be taken to a hospital. What had been done was only temporary even though the man was improving with each respiration.

The Cong cadre who had detained Barnes were both guarded and grateful in demeanor. Stealthily they vanished, blending into the darkness as Barnes cautiously watched their withdrawal out of the corner of his eye. Without captors, Barnes was free to go. So after a final check on the patient who turned out to be a tough old bird, Barnes resumed his trip around the perimeter to the main south gate of the air base—the opposite direction from which the militants had exited the village.

Nothing would be said about this encounter with the enemy except to offer thanks to the Lord. However, in the rush of the emergency, Barnes had almost forgotten why he was on that road in the first place. Almost forgotten! Yet surprisingly, his anger had greatly dissipated by his overwhelming thankfulness to be free and alive.

Barnes entered the main checkpoint gate without incident. The MPs when asked about the rigid rules regarding the special forces gate, acknowledged that the new "commanding" was weird about that particular access point from the Vietnamese compound.

Barnes drove around the inner base road passing within ten feet of the gate in question. Without any hesitation he traveled across the end of the runway and back to the supportive army side of the base—the First Team side, where the word "team" still meant something.

CHAPTER 26

PLAYING GAMES DURING A WAR

Though the level of rage had lessened over a restless night, remembrance of the gate incident fanned the flames of infuriation the next morning, flaring up to infringe upon almost every conscious thought. In the past, Adam Barnes was not known for being prone to moods of bad temper. In fact, the more accurate definition of "temper" as it applied to him would be "calmness of mind, disposed to being outwardly composed." But not this day. He woke up *mad!* Heatedly *mad.* Today he would not be mollified, "tempered" to be calm and composed. Today his mood was mad—purely and simply *mad!* Yet deep down he knew his feelings were exaggeratedly wrong.

"Gastrocnemius! I should have said this. I should have done that. What a bunch of jackleg jerks those air force guys were!"

A more restrained inner voice would counter with, "Stop. Think about it. What was meant for bad was turned into something for good. You survived and so did the old man on the motorbike."

From his upbringing Barnes was aware of scriptural truths like, "Be angry but sin not; do not let the sun set on your anger; vengeance is mine, says the Lord; do not be overcome by evil, but overcome evil with good."

The internal rebuttal to these scriptures reminded Barnes with great regularity that the air force major, whoever he was, had put the army doctor's life in jeopardy by forcing him to go outside the secure confines of the base to enter the *main gate*. "Why couldn't the man make a simple field decision? That's his job as the officer-in-charge. He was the one who had the authority to override the rigidity of that newly instituted restriction about the special forces gate." Barnes was determined to confront the guy face-to-face. That was scriptural too! He would go at lunchtime.

On the way across to the air force base headquarters Captain Barnes rehearsed, over and over, words and phrases with himself. "What should I say? I forgive you? Hardly. It would take a lot of self-control to say that. Man, what were you thinking? I almost got captured. I could have been killed!"

Barnes just wanted to ask him _why_. Why had he refused to make the call to let a fellow American soldier pass? Were they not on the same team? Why so rigid about that gate? Why force a soldier out into the enemy countryside to a distant gate. How thoughtless. Gutless. Weak! What possible explanation could there be for such insanity? And even worse, all this done against a field veteran so near to his DEROS!

The airman first class managing the front desk asked whom the army captain had come to see. Barnes requested to speak with the duty officer who was on call the night before. A search of the monthly roster confirmed the name.

"That would be Major Thornton. He is at lunch but should be back soon. He left around 1130 hours."

Barnes indicated that he would get a quick bite at the air force cafeteria and check back in thirty minutes.

When Barnes returned, the clerk escorted him down the hall to a complex of offices. The airman knocked and announced to the major.

"Captain Barnes of the army is here to see you, sir."

With his hand the escort opened the office door aperture for entry. As Barnes walked through, his eyes widened like the doorway and his mouth dropped with his jaw toward the floor. In a seeming state of suspended animation, he presented a hesitant hand salute in slow motion, still astounded at the figure who sat before him.

"I did not know it was you," he stated.

Major Coy Thornton replied, "I *did* know it was you!"

Then dead silence.

The temperature in the room was already midday hot; but if looks were lasers, Thornton would have been lit up into flames, burnt crispy by the captain's glare. Meanwhile, the smirk on the major's face was malicious, one expressive of contempt.

The feeling of disdain was mutual with Barnes. Here was the man who had never apologized for fracturing his face years before. The very same man who had endangered him to physical harm again just one night ago.

Barnes broke the silence, "Why the gate blockage for me?"

"You're a Dookie," said Thornton arrogantly. "Why the *cheap shot* about being in the field?"

Another prolonged pause without speaking elapsed. Barnes' heart cycled with heaves and poundings. His mouth grew dry and cottony, and his internal anger thermometer was rising rapidly, rocketing up and up and up.

However, in his brain two words reverberated like his skull was an echo chamber. Over and over: *"Sin not. Sin not. Sin not."*

In spite of his verbal rehearsals, Barnes had not strategized an exit speech before his arrival on the air force side of the base. What could he possibly say that was not what he felt? What could he get away with before a superior officer? How far could he push the proverbial envelope? Barnes had a habit of pushing the envelope and then crossing over the line and ticking people off.

At this point all the air in the staff cubicle was sucked out. Only some residual oxygen in the lungs of the two in confrontal attack. They were leering at one another, eyes fiercely focused, each man with his personal weapon system of thought locked in the standby position, ready to fire. The uncomfortably long period of stalemated silence continued.

Then with noticeable tension in his voice and a flush on his face, Adam Barnes proffered, "I apologize for the 'field' remark. It was a cheap shot. Forgive me."

Barnes could not believe the words coming out of his mouth. When he followed up with, "I forgive you for the gate incident last night. Orders are orders. It worked for good," Thornton was caught off guard. He remained seated behind his desk, his head cocked in a position of stunned disbelief.

Captain Barnes recognized this moment of stupefaction. Having recovered from his own bewilderment first, Barnes sharply saluted, made an about face, and left the office immediately. He too was still bedazzled by the words of forgiveness which he had uttered—words from a different Spirit, inspired from a higher-than-human source.

As Barnes drove his jeep back around the Bien Hoa runway to the First Cav side, his post-game analysis was underway. There had been anger but he had not sinned by acting on it. Admittedly the closure was not one that Barnes might have envisioned; but in retrospect, forgiveness was the right thing to do—whether he felt like it or not. Something pulled him back from the brink of a no-win situation. Spitefulness and pettiness thrive as playthings of the ranking powerful in most established institutions. The military was not immune. One swing and a court-martial later, and Barnes would have borne the full brunt of institutional discipline.

As Barnes replayed the office encounter, he speculated on the possibility that Coy Boy may even have been trying to goad him into an assault. Barnes quickly deflected the idea of deliberate provocation because that would have been too dastardly a thing to do, even for a Tar Heel rival.

As the jeep entered the "good" zone, Barnes remembered to flash a belated prayer. "Thanks, Lord, for empowering me with a little self-restraint. Clearly, I needed it. Thanks again!"

The covetous competition of the army with the air force could easily be stirred up out of the "wild blue yonder" by just a hint of righteous arrogance from either branch. The intensity could be upped a notch simply by hearing one disparaging word as among the rival "Cameron Crazies" of Duke or the true "blue bloods" of North Carolina in the ACC. From Barnes' perspective the air force facilities overseas were always superior to the army accommodations. Everything first class. Number ten. The air force could scrounge the best clinic equipment and laboratory resources for their physicians; and their special services programs of recreation were outstanding.

For the air force, coming southwest inland from Cam Ranh Bay on the South China seashore to an assignment at Bien Hoa air base above Saigon was considered earning one's "combat pay" by airmen. It was hard for Barnes to imagine that the army's rear base would be considered the air force's combat zone. Now Barnes would not belittle the value air support provided the grunts (infantrymen) on the ground; but in his mind the question he posed to Thornton was a valid one when he asked, "Have you ever been in the field?" A significant combat difference did exist between Peanuts cartoon character Snoopy portraying a World War I Sopwith Camel pilot in the air and Charlie Brown's pet Snoopy walking as a dog in the trenches on the ground.

In the last month of Barnes' tour of duty in Vietnam, the rivalry between the two military corps intensified locally with a unique on-the-field opportunity like the army-navy game in college football. An inter-service basketball tournament was proposed by the special services division of both branches—a mini Final Four. The games would be played at Bien Hoa in the thousand-seat hangar/arena on the premises of the air base. Four teams would be assembled, one each from the Ninth Infantry (army), the First Cav (army), Tan Son Nhut air base, and the Bien Hoa air base, (the odds-on favorite being the host team since they were the reigning and undefeated champions).

Most of the hastily assembled teams for the tournament had a smattering of former high school or collegiate players. The only guys the First Team had were mostly 15th Medical Battalion gym-rat types. Adam Barnes was recruited and he pulled in his old rival Brian Jenner to bolster the experience of the army team. This assemblage of players for the cavalrymen was small in numbers and small in stature. At six-foot-three, Barnes was the tallest player for his team. Collegiately, he had been a point guard. Here he would have to defend as a center.

The CAV athletes adopted the moniker, "G-Runts," as a motivational name because of their lack of size (remembering Adolph "Rupp's runts" of 1966 Kentucky fame; no starting player on that team was over six foot five.) Furthermore, the army team chose the name as a point of respect for the "field foot soldiers" who affectionately referred to themselves as "grunts."

A piece of dramatic irony came with the starting lineup of the Bien Hoa flyer's team. The six-foot-eight-inch giant center for the host team was none other than *Coy Thornton,* Barnes' Tar Heel antagonist. He was "stodgy" like Barnes but here the reference defined his bulky, bullying physical build. Coy Boy tipped the Toledos at 250 pounds; Barnes was a mere 175.

The brackets for the tournament were arranged so that the finals would pit an army team against an air force opponent. Both the G-Runts and Bien Hoa made it into that final game, set for a Saturday night. The majority of the fans were air force personnel, but playing before a hostile crowd was nothing new for Jenner and Barnes. After the Big Four battles on "Tobacco Road" and two Final Fours for Barnes, this clamorous environ embodied nothing new for these two veterans of court wars.

The championship game initially was dominated as expected by the brute size of the air force team which repeatedly pounded the ball inside. The CAV foul count was going up early on this seven-man squad. Since this was the home court for the Bien Hoa team, and since the unit was familiar with the various idiosyncrasies of their teammates, having played together regularly over the past six months, they executed their game plan with precision passing and high-percentage post scoring. At halftime, the

G-Runts were lucky to be down only by ten points, 40 to 30.

At the start of the second half, the army team incorporated a swarming, pressure defense, full court. Quickness contributed to three successive steals drawing the CAV to within four points, a deficit which persisted during the first five minutes of the second half. Additional costly fouls forced the G-Runts to switch to a two-three zone defense to protect those players with four fouls—two of the five starters at that time. Barnes already had three personal fouls trying to keep the towering Thornton out of the painted key.

A sequence of traps sprung in the corners of the zone defense resulted in two fast breaks to tie the score at fifty with ten minutes remaining in the game. From that point the lead changed hands a half-dozen or so times as tired legs began to impact the shooting accuracy of both teams. However, the size of the air force players was allowing them to score with greater ease than the army team, especially inside around the rim.

Two army players fouled out midway through the second half, leaving only five eligible players on the army squad. Three minutes remained on the clock. The score was knotted at 68 apiece.

To keep from fouling out a third army player and to take advantage of the absence of the "professional" shot clock, putting the ball into a deep freeze seemed to be a warranted approach. The hope was to shorten the game without fouling and to get off a winning shot at the buzzer. Overtime would not be a bad alternative if the shot missed.

Brian Jenner called for a G-Runt time out, the first one of the half. In the huddle he suggested a bizarre strategy for managing the clock. He had heard about a tactic developed by UNC Coach Dean Smith and designated the Four Corners. This unique system of offense utilized the whole half-court by positioning four players in the corners with the fifth and best ball handler working in the middle above the top of the key. He diagrammed it in the coating of red clay dust on the floor. This spread originally was implemented as a stalling device but proved, as it was perfected, to be an effective offensive-style weapon. The floor opened up for back-door cut layups and easy dribble-drives to the basket for scores.

Coy Boy was also familiar with this Carolina stratagem. He recognized the "Four Corners" right off and when the ball was deflected out of bounds, he called time out to discuss the maneuver with his teammates.

As the air force returned for the inbounds play by the army, they dropped back into what was called a box-and-one defense with a chosen player hounding Barnes all over the court.

With ninety seconds to play and the score still tied, Barnes' shadow defender deliberately fouled him while feigning a steal of the dribble. The one-and-one rule was in effect so Barnes went to the free throw line to shoot. The pressure was on to sink the first shot and get the bonus. He missed. The ball spun off the back of the rim, drifting to the left and into the huge-hand clutches of Coy Boy. The major's smirk was back like that day in his office. His strategy of an intentional foul had worked. His team had the ball and the question was would the air force hold it for the last shot too?

Without any slowing of play the airmen immediately went down court overloading the right side of the army's two-three zone. Barnes as the G-Runt center was attempting to front Thornton in the key, but he had four fouls.

One cross-court throw and a precision-lob pass later, the ball found its way overhead to Thornton. With a drop-step pivot, he banked home an easy lay-up. Barnes had had to pull back in fear of being called for his fifth foul, the disqualifying one. The score was air force 70, army 68.

With the subsequent inbounds pass, Barnes brought the ball up the court. He crossed the mid-court line with one minute to play. The plan, as before, was for him to handle the ball for fifty seconds, passing off, and getting the ball back in the middle to avoid the double teaming. With ten seconds to go in the game, Barnes would retrieve the ball at the top of the key. The other four team members would dive to the baseline, flaring out to the corners, thus clearing the floor for Barnes to go one-on-one for the final shot and a possible "and-one" foul. In the case of a miss, a few seconds would be left for a rebounded put-back or a tip-in basket to create an overtime situation.

Playing for a tie even with the possibility of an overtime period was a distasteful concept to Barnes. In truth he knew his team would be hard pressed to win an overtime game in light of their limited manpower circumstances. Realistically, they could not afford to let their opponents have the ball again on offense considering the air force's dominance inside and the fragile foul status of the G-Runts.

At first, no one came out to guard Barnes, so he just stood there, "yo-yoing" the ball while facing the basket straight on. The temptation was great to take the open shot early. The clock inched down to forty seconds.

When the air force players sensed that the army team was strangely playing for the last shot, they cautiously edged out forcing the Four Corners passing process to start. Barnes would pass off to the side and then immediately retrieve the ball back since the air force zone remained packed tight. He dribble-drove toward the foul line as if attacking; then when blocked, he passed to the opposite corner getting the ball back with an up-close hand off. With each return transfer possession of the ball, Barnes had every option available to him. Facing the basket in the triple-threat position, it would be his discretion in the final seconds as to when and whether to pass, drive, or shoot.

Though ahead on the scoreboard, Coy Thornton was visibly frustrated. With thirty seconds to go, an errant pass was intercepted by an airman defender, but his foot touched the out of bounds line. Possession went back to the army. Quickly, Thornton called timeout, their second.

Thornton knew from experience of Barnes' prowess as a spot-up, outside shooter. Gesturing emphatically with his hands, his index finger pointed forcibly toward spots on the court. First here, then there. He instructed the guard covering Barnes to deny the pull-up jump shot and to herd him left saying, "Make Barnes drive the lane and I'll do the rest!" Thornton had previously smacked five shots up into the stands already that night.

When play resumed, Coy Boy anchored himself to the right of the point, sloughing off his man who was positioned deep in the corner. The ball was inbounded to Barnes in the backcourt. With the dribble, he centered play at the top of the key. His defender squatted down like a spider stalking its entangled prey. His exaggerated positioning forced Barnes to the left. Twenty seconds to go and counting.

Smothering pressure on the four men in the corners hindered the give-and-go process. Open passing exchanges were nearly impossible. Every pass was contested.

Barnes kept his dribble alive, reversing sharply to the right elbow of the foul line. The defenders of Jenner attempted a double team, exposing a passing lane. Barnes dropped a one hand bounce pass to Jenner. Fifteen seconds left. Jenner made a ball fake to the right corner and Thornton bit on the feint by sliding out toward his man. Jenner snapped off a two-handed chest pass back to Barnes, centered above the arc. *Ten seconds.*

About this time, as per design, all four of the other army players made slashing cuts to the baseline. No one was open. From there they drifted out to the edges opening up the floor. *Eight seconds!*

Barnes jabbed his left foot out as a powerful bull might paw the ground before charging. His defender opened up his stance like a gate. Barnes "rockered" back into set-shot position as if preparing to rise up for a jump shot. *Five seconds!* The defender's weight shifted forward on his toes allowing Barnes to explode left with a giant drive-step dribble to the basket. The lane was clear for an unmolested lay-in.

Then, out of the corner of his right eye Barnes saw Thornton striding toward him for the block. Barnes was determined. Thornton was determined. A colossal collision appeared imminent.

The doctor cradled the ball firmly between his right palm and his inner forearm and mounted up in flight on the right side of the rim. Thornton's monstrous wing span came swooping for a spiking swat of the basketball as soon as it was released. This was déjà vu for Barnes. *Three seconds. Two seconds.*

At the very last instant, Barnes ripped the ball down beneath the rim from the right and rotated his body in midair. He spun 90 degrees counter clockwise, preparing his back for the inevitable collision of airborne objects. Absorbing the impactive impetus from Thornton's torso, Barnes completed an arc under the net with his arm and up beyond the opposite side of the rim.

Thornton's palm smashed into the orange goal's edge while

the ball squirted up as a feathery finger roll shot off the back-board, high on the left side. Two seconds. One second. The ball caromed out to the front of the rim. One bounce off the metal sent it straight up. The second bounce off the front edge directed the ball back toward the board causing it to make a kissing contact above the square.

Thornton's momentum had carried him hard, right through Barnes, and the two men went sprawling into the padded goal support beyond the baseline. In the background two distinct sounds could be heard.

First, the horn had gone off signifying the end of the game. It sounded like a Mack truck. Yet the ball was still rebounding high above the cylinder. One more caress of the rim and it nestled down through the net with a splash. "Whoosh." Game tied. Overtime? But No!

The second sound was a whistle, a referee's whistle. A foul had been called on the air force's Thornton. One shot for victory. This time Barnes would have the opportunity to shoot his own free throw for the undefeated "walk-off win."

The Bien Hoa team took their final time out for the purpose of icing Barnes. They meant it for bad but it worked for Barnes' good. His right elbow had taken the full impact of the basket support. He needed the extra time to get sensation restored along the innervations of the "crazy bone."

Three dribbles, a silent prayer (TIBIA), the fingertip release, the follow-through, and the ball disappeared with a "swish" through the net. Game over; still *undefeated!*

As Barnes passed Thornton, he extended his hand without comment. The major responded firmly, pulling Barnes face-to-face. He mouthed, "My fault...my fault. Good game."

Barnes was uncertain whether that was a reference to the final hard foul or to the ARVN gate issue. He chose to receive it with grace and moved on toward the locker room. It seemed sad to Barnes that two American warriors fighting for the same purpose could not be on the same team. ***But Vietnam was not a game. It was a war!***

CHAPTER 27

CAMBODIA AND KENT STATE

I n the spring of 1970, campus turmoil against the war took a turn for the worse. President Richard Nixon had ordered intensive bombing attacks—for some time advocated by the Joint Chiefs of Staff—against the NVA sanctuaries in Cambodia. The silent majority of the U.S. populace had discovered their voice in the latter months of 1969 and in the later winter days of 1970. Solid support for Nixon's policies did exist outside the Capital Beltway of D.C., but in Congress and on the college campuses, another perspective was sounding the dominant tone: a whining tone—histrionic, hysterical, and hateful.

The Vietnamization process was described by some observers to be making substantial gains. The southern countryside was more secure than at any time since the Tet Offensive. With the insurgency seemingly under control, Nixon listened to the concerns of the battlefield commanders to neutralize the "neutral" border of Cambodia. It was believed that an attack on the North Vietnamese embedment would provide a cushion of time for the borders of South Vietnam to be strengthened further by an infusion of ARVN troops.

President Nixon's plan initially called for a brief surge by

American soldiers into the Fishhook area in III CORPS. The First Air Cav would be a primary player in this incursion strategy.

The region to be flooded with U.S. infantry was located fifty-five miles northwest of Saigon. It was estimated that three North Vietnamese divisions still were camped in the area with all their supplies having been built up over the last years while Cambodia turned a blind eye. The NVA was using these safe sanctuary sites to launch sporadic, hit-and-run assaults on American landing zones near the border.

With this incursion, President Nixon hoped to provide some stabilization for the new Lon Nol regime in Cambodia, to influence Hanoi to resume peace negotiations and, most importantly, to protect U.S. soldiers in the region as unit withdrawals began. The "boots on the ground" understood firsthand this need for the shielding cushion for themselves and for buying time for the South Vietnamese forces.

Therefore, in a speech to the nation on April 30, 1970, the president laid out his plan to the American people. Nixon was cognizant of the potential for civilian and student protests in response to such an announcement; but he was resolute against such intimidation. He fervently acknowledged that he would rather be a one-term president than preside over America's first major wartime defeat. In addition, he was quite adamant that this mission would be short-lived, less than two months. Nixon underestimated the domestic reaction.

Certain leadership from the protestors, the politicians, and the public media chose not to believe the spoken word of the commander in chief, but rather clung to the propagandistic pronouncements of the Hanoi hierarchy. Once again, anchorman C.K. Walters and Senator Bright contributed to stateside confusion by broadcasting statements to the effect that "the United States *may* have invaded the sovereign nation of Cambodia and thus may have expanded the war!" Egregiously, they decided not to take the U.S. President at his word concerning the timeline for ending the incursion. Demonstrations erupted on college campuses as if on cue, and National Guard Troops in certain situations were dispatched to keep order. Some in academia could not wait four days to evaluate the truth of the President's word on the conduct of this operational surge into Cambodia. Tragically, four students at Kent State University in Akron, Ohio (near where Doctor Barnes interned) were killed in the campus chaos instigated by believing the propaganda of the enemy against the promises of their own elected officials—promises this particular time that were kept.

If only the faithless factions could have heard the truth from someone who was stationed on the Cambodian border, that terrible campus tragedy could have been averted. If only the protesting public had just trusted for sixty days, four young adults would still be alive—and students at Adam's alma mater might not have chosen at graduation to wear white armbands in protest, thus inadvertently supporting the enemy against one of their own. (Within a decade, more than a million civilians will have died in the communist "killing fields" of Cambodia.) Meanwhile, Barnes was wondering how this tragic turn of events in Akron could have been prevented.

Just as President Nixon promised, the incursion ended in two months with American forces withdrawing from Cambodia by the end of June—to the day.

In the middle of the surge mission, DEROS day came for Captain Adam Barnes. It was June 15th! The short-timers calendar was completely colored in with magic marker. The Date of Estimated Return from Overseas duty was at hand. Twenty-four hours and a wake-up.

CHAPTER 28

DEROS DAY FOR THE DOC

Only one more bugle reveille for Barnes. The sun was shining; the sky was blue. Rays of light came beaming in across the living quarters. They illuminated the flecks and specks of red clay dust whimsically dancing on the swirling currents of warming air. A rub of the eyes and a bound from the bed signaled the beginning of the final twenty-four hours in Vietnam. The captain physician started the day off right with a full breakfast.

The formal steps for ending a tour of duty in the 15th Med Battalion were as follows: fly back to Phuoc Vinh to collect one's records; return to Bien Hoa Cav headquarters to pack and muster out with Temporary Duty Assignment (TDY) orders for the states; take the bus to the air base departure section; and fly home via Guam to San Francisco where it all started about a year ago.

At the controls that morning, Chief Warrant Officer, Rod Edwards, piloted the LOCH plane. His was a new face to the DEROSing doctor. All the aviators which Barnes knew were actively participating on the Cambodian scene of operations. The trip out was short and sweet, approaching Phuoc Vinh from the east. The terrain seemed so familiar from above. Phuoc Hua I

227

and Phuoc Hua II, even Nui Ba Dinh and Nui Ba Ra were faintly visible in the distance.

As they were beginning their descent, something ricocheted off the tail rotor emitting a sharp, metallic ping. Edwards adroitly maneuvered the aircraft to a soft touch down in a nearby clearing. After checking the rear, he reported that a panel screw was missing from one of the tail flaps on the left.

Nonchalantly he took a roll of bandage tape from the tool kit under his seat. "It happens all the time. No problem."

For an instant, his unflappable demeanor reminded Barnes of pilot Cutty's "cool" in the early days of his tour. The flight resumed without incident and soon they were again on the MEDEVAC tarmac at the Phuoc Vinh base.

Arriving around noon, the two men shared a final lunch with the few remaining staff acquaintances at 15th Med. The doctors and medics who had made up the team when Barnes was assigned to this clearing company had all left country on earlier DEROS days. However, one enlisted specialist who competed with Barnes regularly out the backdoor of the mess hall on the worn-down dust bowl of a basketball court was still there.

Specialist Mickey Jordan was jokingly upset that he had never been on a team to beat Barnes during his tour at 15th Med. He even challenged Barnes to one final game of one-on-one. The captain chose to stay undefeated so he declined with a smile.

All appropriate signatures on transfer documents completed, it was time to saddle up one final time and head back south toward the rear echelon Admin Unit of the CAV. It was a beautiful day to fly that final in-country flight. Clear and calm, free as a bird—almost.

The chopper had become hot and the red dust began to swirl and in an instant they were aloft over Phuoc Vinh. Barnes could observe his old artillery unit firing support to the west. Their 155mm howitzers provided the only puff of clouds in the air.

Reaching an altitude of 1,000 feet, Barnes relaxed and closed his eyes. That never would have happened on any other duty day. He had completed his day-to-days and was going home.

Interrupting the drowse-inducing drone, the radio came on, and the pilot intently listened. The message detailed a medical emergency and was requesting a MEDEVAC to come to Nui Ba Dinh. There had been a vehicle accident and one of the missionaries had been hurt. Since all the dust-off helicopters were actively engaged with supporting the infantry CAV units in the Fishhook campaign, the request was being made to any chopper in the vicinity to help transport the injured person to Saigon. This trip, of course, meant a flight toward the Cambodian border, slightly North of the Fishhook.

As the ranking officer in the plane, Barnes was asked by the pilot as to what they should do. Without hesitation, Barnes replied for the pilot to head north immediately, then west to the mount of Nui Ba Dinh. Based on the initial phone contact from the orphanage, the caller had expressed grave concern, if not true panic, over the situation—something about serious head trauma and worsening signs and symptoms. Urgent and timely hospital treatment seemed indicated. Barnes apprehensively pondered the possibility, "Could the injured one be Claire?"

It was about two o'clock when the LOCH put down in an open play area beside the mission school. Claire did not come out to greet them. The children were gathered in the dining hall. The director of the orphanage, a Vietnamese minister who had studied in the States at Fuller Seminary, was the first person Barnes recognized from his occasional trips to visit Claire.

Entering the clinic, Barnes' eye caught a glimpse of a woman lying on a canvas cot behind a screen. Moving the netting back, he saw Claire with a gauze-wrapped headband. The compress dressing was mildly saturated with blood. She smiled as he leaned in to take her hand and instinctively check her pulse. It was full, but slower than normal. There was the residual of an episode of vomiting on her blouse, and her breathing was slowed. Barnes' words to her were simple but reassuring. He tenderly touched her forehead and prayed silently, "Lord, help her and thank you in advance, Father."

The Montagnard director quickly recounted how the injury supposedly occurred. "A few days ago Nurse Claire was riding in the jeep, passenger side, on her way to a local hamlet. The jeep had been used to convey supplies for the mission earlier that morning, which required the front passenger seat be unhooked and folded to create more room for stowing in the back. After the supplies were unloaded, the driver forgot to refasten the cotter pin properly to secure the seat.

"Later, when Nurse Claire was riding down the mountain, a bump in the road in the middle of a curve caused her to be eject-ed out of the jeep. She rolled a short distance and then struck her head on a guardrail boulder put there to keep vehicles from sliding over the edge during the monsoon season. She was briefly unconscious," the driver said, "but soon came around.

"Back here we cleaned her abrasions and bandaged her head. She had a small laceration in the scalp too. We thought she was doing better. Then suddenly this morning she lost consciousness and went into a seizure. That's when she threw up on her clothes.

The seizure lasted only a short time and she seemed to recover fully. At that point her instructions were for us to try and get a MEDEVAC from the U.S. Army. That was an hour ago."

Other than being slightly lethargic, Claire Marshall appeared to be stable. Her pupils were normal and responsive. However, her temperature was going up. A cerebral hemorrhage or cerebral edema from the concussion were possibilities. With physical diagnosis and observation being his only tools—no x-ray or angiography, Barnes knew his friend Claire needed a hospital for more definitive evaluation and care, and she needed it yesterday.

Immediately, Barnes stepped outside and told his pilot to prepare the helicopter's backseat area for a passenger on a cot. Raising and latching the seat against the wall provided floor space that would easily accommodate a stretcher. Quickly, the adaptation of the back area was completed and Claire was seatbelted down in a supine position. The cot was then additionally secured to the floor with cargo straps. In little under an hour, she would be at an evacuation hospital, Barnes estimated.

CHAPTER 29

FLIGHT FOR A LIFE

The sun glared golden through the plexiglass canopy. It was now mid-afternoon. Doctor Barnes would have preferred to travel kneeling cot-side to his patient, but the stretcher afforded only cramped access for a second person. From his copilot's seat on the left, Barnes could monitor Claire's facial expressions and any upper torso distress through the vertical gap in the partitioned cockpit.

Liftoff of the helicopter from the schoolyard was deliberately slow and gentle. Yet the blade-wash rebounding off the orphanage buildings caused Claire's exposed blond hair to take on that wind blown look—the look of a baseball-capped, female jogger trapped in a sudden mini-twister spiraling up out of the dirt in her path. A similar spiraling ascent would have been the safer course for takeoff considering the possibility of hostile activity in the area. Yet under the circumstances a more gradual banking pattern was better for the comfort of the patient.

As the copter gained altitude above the mission, Claire smiled a helpless smile back toward the waving children then squinted her eyes shut as a defense against the flying particles of dust. For the sake of time, it was decided to head due south toward Tay Ninh, a closer medical care center than Saigon.

Gliding out off the mountain and beginning a steady and less turbulent climb, the engine hum was interrupted by a succession of metallic pings. With the first ping, Barnes turned to view the tail flaps. With the second and third, the chopper lurched to the left as Edwards slumped forward in his straps. The pilot had been shot by sniper fire up through the chopper floor. The pings were from a brief barrage of bullets striking the belly of the fuselage. Barnes could see his pilot had been struck in the head and chest. The head wound had resulted in his collapsing unconscious.

A quick glance from Barnes revealed that Claire seemed unharmed but her eyes were filled with terror. Then they closed. Had she too been hit? Barnes feared she had.

The helicopter was arching like a roller coaster car going over the top of the first drop on the ride. Audibly, Barnes uttered his standard flash prayer. After a few explosive expletives of "Gastrocnemius!" came, "Lord, help us...TIBIA."

Mason Huneycutt came to mind. Barnes remembered what his first chopper chauffeur with the CAV had taught him, *step one:* "Grasp the joy stick and get control of the bird. Balance on the tightrope." This emergency was worse than the worst he had ever imagined back then.

With one forceful jerk, Barnes pulled Edwards back in his seat, freeing the control stick on the right. The helicopter started to climb toward a nose-up position. Barnes latched on to his control stick and inadvertently overcompensated to the left. "Do everything slow. Slow down." He could hear that voice in his head, *"Get control first!"*

The ascending attitude continued; the direction: southwest

toward Cambodia. Barnes knew he needed to level off. He also needed to be traveling southeast. First things first. Get level with the land below. How? His so-called "training" exercise had started on a horizontal plane; there was nothing about getting to level from up or down. Deceleration was all Barnes knew. "That might work," he thought. Barnes took a deep breath and peeked over his right shoulder at Claire. Her eyes remained shut; her body was limp, but one responding heave of her chest indicated to him she was alive.

Step two: "Slow the aircraft down." Barnes reached out his right palm and ever so gingerly depressed the tip of the throttle pipe. The chopper's nose came down, now flatly aligned to the ground (relaxation). Soon the bubble slipped below the line on the gauge. The helicopter was descending too fast (tension). Then, as if an external force had tipped it back, the aircraft was on a horizontal plane again (peace). There was only one problem. The ship was still flying in the wrong direction.

Based on the position of the sun in the sky, the helicopter was heading straight for Cambodia. Barnes decided to fly with the flow. The alternative was to fly off in a panic. At that point in the saga he felt that he had no choice because he was quite hesitant to attempt any experimentation with the flight controls. He was flying level and he might even come across some U.S. troops advancing on the border—a plus for sure. An uninterrupted time to think was a dire necessity. "Lord, help!"

Claire moved an extremity, creating a clunking sound in back as her arm made contact with a restraining clamp. One of the straps securing the stretcher had loosened. In his stream of consciousness, Barnes kept grounding himself on the flight emergency instructions of Mason Huneycutt. He wished that

Cutty's premonitory statements could have embraced flexibility as opposed to inevitability: *"You crash! That's your best chance of survival!"*

A crash landing conjured up disaster images from the media and motion pictures—a waste of mental energy for Barnes. He refocused. "What about Claire? Could I land the chopper safely and beat the odds? Lord, help me. TIBIA. TIBIA. TIBIA!"

A dawn of calm crept over Barnes. "One way or the other, it would be all right." In the live or die rivalry of human existence, for a Christian, death is never defeat. The acting pilot and his patient were both prepared for eternity as believers in Christ. In the scripture which stated, "And inasmuch as it is appointed…once to die…" (Heb 9:27), that "once-to-die person" had a DEROS: Date Estimated for Return of One's *Soul*. Barnes was hopeful that today would not be his recall day, but he was ready if it was. Only God knew the exact date and time of his going home.

The successful land "ditching" of the aircraft was the paramount issue at hand. Sooner rather than later was Barnes' decision. Before he could change his mind, his right hand released the shared grip on the control stick and hovered with an open palm above the throttle. Last chance, no? Deliberately Barnes depressed the rod in very slight increments until the chopper began to descend. At the time their course was out over an elephant-grass-covered plain. The helicopter was about fifteen hundred feet above the ground.

As the altimeter read one thousand feet, the initial landing zone field flashed below then behind; and a multi-terraced valley of rice paddies appeared but quickly was also overflown. An adjacent valley held more promise but thickly canopied slopes were menacingly close. Since Barnes had no specific control over where the helicopter would touch down, a crash point in the center of the rice paddy seemed to be an optimal target—500 feet to black water or red clay.

A line of trees was coming up fast at the southern edge of the rice field. The angle of descent was about 20 to 30 degrees and they were now flying too low to see what the terrain was like on the other side. The ground vegetation and the surface stubble of rice husks in the ponds were becoming blurred as the whirlybird LOCH whooshed by. Barnes reasoned that if they could clear the trees and if earthen levees and more rice pools were on the other side, the crash would be cushioned somewhat.

The curled up skids of the chopper's runners just grazed the top of a row of bamboo trees. The glide path looked clear ahead revealing a 400-foot-long "runway" of paddies. If the flight lasted longer (four hundred one feet) a grove of bamboo would be harvested into shoots and splinters by the rotating blades. The chopper would be chopping wood at a new angle of attack. "Lord, help us! We're going in!"

The initial impact emitted a violent thump. The collision with the paddy pool raised a wall of water up into the twirling blades. The wave was pushing one gigantic tide until the forward circumference arc of the overhead propeller made contact with a levee ridge. Splash, crash, crack! The airfoils smacked the water like flat paddles and snapped at their midpoints. Bits and pieces were sent hurling in every direction. The body of the copter launched, being vaulted by the rotating hub and blade nubs. The tail rotor buckled and broke off as the fuselage came to rest on its side with a thud.

Just before striking the water, Barnes had thrust the throttle flat down to the off position. In the violent force of the crash, his left ankle had become wedged between the foot pedals. With some adrenalin-aided strength, he was able to free his leg by removing his boot and to twist out of his seat on the sunken side of the chopper. Edwards was still strapped in the pilot's seat. As Barnes climbed over his body to exit, he checked for signs of life. There were none. The next priority was to get Claire out and away from the wreck. She was suspended upright with her head positioned in the un-submerged doorway. She had been so tightly secured with wrapped blankets and canvas cords to the stretcher, and the stretcher, to the floor, that the cockpit capsule had functioned as a roll cage.

After releasing the belts which anchored the stretcher to steel frames, Barnes made one all-out effort to hoist Claire out. His leverage was poor because of the LOCH's angle of lean and his first attempt failed. He would have to rig something or get some help.

For Claire, being unconscious held a double blessing. Her limp body was enabled to absorb the forces which battered the external shell of the ship, and her recollection of the crash would be probably lost in a state of post-traumatic amnesia.

Out of the corner of his eye, Barnes detected movement along the levees. Figures were approaching from a nearby hamlet. He hoped they were farmers…they were not.

Within minutes pajama-clad soldiers of the Viet Cong surrounded the downed aircraft. All Barnes had for defense was a .45-caliber pistol, a gun he had never really learned to fire since, until he turned it in, his primary weapon had been the M16. Regarding the use of the .45 in a fight, his best option would have been to throw it at the enemy. For him, that would have been the more accurate choice, but with only one gun he chose to forego that option. He slowly placed the gun, still in its holster, on the levee ridge and raised his hands.

"Chieu Hoi, Chieu Hoi," came the words of surrender out of his mouth. He repeated them as he pointed to Claire, only partially visible inside the copter.

Soon Claire Marshall's stretcher was being extricated with care from the crumpled aircraft, and two Vietnamese villagers carried it toward the town. After both his wrists were lashed together in front and his arms immobilized with a bamboo pole inserted between the elbow joints across the back, Barnes was led away with a hemp rope noosed around his neck.

Claire was alive, semi-comatose, and still in urgent need of immediate care. Barnes was a prisoner of war on his DEROS day.

CHAPTER 30

THE UNDERWORLD IS ALIVE

Camouflaged amidst the overgrowth of a triple-canopy jungle, the enemy encampment included several sheet metal hooches and canvas tents. These disguised additions blended in well beside the permanent village structures in this civilian no-fire zone. The name of the province was Duc Phong, which just happened to be in the border region described in the report of the LRRP group. Some time back that squad had inadvertently stumbled onto an NVA complex of bunkers, schools, and an underground hospital. Barnes had treated the wounds of members of this recon unit at 15th Med after their skirmish with the North Vietnamese.

As the enemy stretcher bearers approached the hamlet from the rice field, Claire Marshall's body began twitching. Her arms and legs jerked as they extended, feet flexed and toes pointed. A generalized convulsion ensued. Her back arched up off the cot in a rigid spasm. To prevent her from rolling off, the villagers put the litter down on the berm pathway just beyond the final flooded field.

Barnes immediately bolted off the levee into the end corner of the mire square, yanking the guide line out of the grip of the guard. He collapsed into the paddy slope dislodging the pole from the crook of his left elbow. Inhaling deeply, he finished extracting the pole from behind his back and came up out of the ditch wielding the staff as a weapon. The path between Claire and Barnes cleared as he brandished the bamboo pipe over his head. He made his way to her side unchallenged.

Laying the staff down, he cupped her face with his fingers, his hands still bound together with a two foot piece of twine. He moved to cradle and support her head in his lap. Her eyes rolled, rotating upward for a brief moment. When the seizure subsided, muscle tone was restored and her eyes resumed a centered gaze though staring distantly off into a cloudless sky. Barnes noticed her pupils, the right slightly dilated in comparison to the left. He feared that she was hemorrhaging intracranially. The crash landing, no doubt, had jostled some clotted capillaries in the brain. Renewed bleeding from damaged blood vessels along with the concurrent build-up of pressure within the skull had in all probability triggered the most recent grand mal seizure.

Prisoner Barnes began shouting in English, demanding that his captors take his companion to their field hospital. The Viet Cong soldiers appeared stunned by the authoritative and desperate tone of the request and stood frozen, puzzled as to what to do next. The spasmodic convulsing of Claire's body clearly had unnerved the unseasoned soldiers in the group.

The clamor in the courtyard summoned the Cong commander from a nearby hut. As he strode toward the army doctor, who was squatting on the ground in a crouched posture supporting his friend's head on his thigh, the enemy officer's pace slowed. He hesitated and then abruptly stopped a few yards away. As the leader resumed his approach, Barnes looked up at the shadowy figure silhouetted by the western sun. Something was familiar

THE UNDERWORLD IS ALIVE

about the man's carriage and his gait. MEDCAPS? The Chieu Hoi program? Barnes was sure he knew this Vietnamese man from somewhere.

While deliberately circling the couple on the ground, the Cong cadre officer stopped again with his back to Barnes, then pivoted about. His new position in the sun manifested his facial features more distinctly. The disfiguring scar above the soldier's upper lip confirmed Barnes' sense of recognition. This officer was the one on whom the surgeon had attempted a cosmetic closure of his wounds after that vicious, slashing attack at the Phuoc Vinh Chieu Hoi camp. The skin laceration had healed but the residual subcutaneous adhesions had drawn the musculature of the mouth on the right side into a gnarled scowl. Both men were taken aback by this unanticipated face-to-face reunion.

Casting a cursory glance at the woman, Major Thieu Chai directed with a pointing gesture toward Barnes. "Bac si…I remember." There was no body language indication whether that was a positive or a negative recollection.

Barnes quickly replied, "Major, this woman is the missionary nurse at the Nui Ba Dinh orphanage. She has a serious head injury. She needs to get to a hospital fast or she will die!"

His voice trailed off to a trembling whisper with that final phrase. Claire was more than just a friend.

Waving his hand for his comrades to step back from their crowded enclosing, Major Thieu sliced the cord cuffs apart with a machete, unbinding Barnes. Mutual respect was being visually demonstrated by these two adversaries.

Thieu responded next, "The nurse, I know."

Then without expression other than what was facially permanent, he declared, "No hospital here."

With an incredulous look, Barnes countered, "But our intelligence says there is. The North Vietnamese have an underground hospital in one of these mountains. I can use their facilities to save her." Barnes gazed down at Claire and tenderly stroked her bandaged temple affirming, "No enemy here."

The Cong major barked an order in Vietnamese and a dilapidated Ford truck was brought forth. Still on the litter, Claire was placed in the flatbed of the truck. After Barnes' wrists were rebound behind his back, he was assisted up onto the lowered tailgate and shuffled to a bench seat that ran along the inside. Three other soldiers with AK-47s piled into the rear taking the opposing side seats. Major Thieu rode in the cab.

Claire remained in a semi-comatose state, responding only intermittently to her environment when stimulated by loud noise or painful jarring of her body as they traversed the bumpy dirt roads toward the Cambodian border. On the way they crossed two makeshift bamboo bridges and passed at least three enemy checkpoints, the final one being manned by whom Barnes recognized as NVA regular troops.

Out in the middle of nowhere, the terrain became rugged and hilly. The truck came to a stop. Major Thieu disappeared into the bamboo-dense jungle. He was gone less than five minutes when he returned, to the astonishment of Barnes, with two blonde haired, blue-eyed females, wearing loose fitting surgical outfits and a North Vietnamese medic wearing a white scrub T-shirt. (The women were nurses, probably of Scandinavian descent. Ruling out Norway and Denmark, Barnes guessed they were Swedish nationals based on their accents.)

With the assistance of the medic and one of the Viet Cong guards, Claire was transported into the thicket and toward a mound overgrown with elephant grass. What appeared to be just another cleverly camouflaged bunker turned out to be a secret tunnel entrance to an enemy camp. The uncleared canopy of trees covered the compound like an overarching umbrella, blocking out any definitive detection from above. Thatched-roof huts, rice hooches, storage sheds, and lean-to caches were interspersed among the tree trunks, hidden stealthily amidst the natural surroundings. Palm thatchings served further to obscure the simplest of structures while strategically placed bunkers were protected from overhead with three feet of layered dirt before the hatchings were applied. And yet, this was only the surface component to a much larger and deeper complex, intricately engineered and all underground.

The entourage moving Claire dissected through another grove of bamboo and vanished down into an excavated trench. It led to a reinforced mine-like opening. The group of soldiers marshaling Barnes diverted to a nearby bunker with a spider-hole ingress to another set of tunnel passageways. Barnes objected to the separation from Claire but was pushed into the hole. The aperture seemed to Barnes barely able to accommodate the diminutive guard who snaked in ahead of him, much less someone his own size. He wondered, "If the impending underground adventure was designed to menace and intimidate the prisoner, it surely was working on this American."

The spreading streaks of late afternoon shadows were creeping through the triple canopy which concealed this alternate entry. Barnes stood up in the hole. Just the mere thought of crawling underground was drenching his shirt with nervous perspiration. He was more terrified of this tunnel trek than of death itself, even though he had observed his predecessor adeptly pass through the narrow opening in the ground. Barnes balked. A stern gesture from the barrel of an AK-47 indicated that the prisoner was to crawl, head first, after the first man.

Barnes dropped to his knees, prayed, and slipped into the gap located flush with the dirt floor. It swallowed him up whole like Jonah and the whale. Almost immediately, the channel widened. The enlargement allowed him eventually to move like an underground coal miner, bent over at the waist, plodding along a horizontal mine shaft to the ore extraction point. However, unbeknownst to Barnes, the last forty to fifty feet would taper down to an anxiety-eliciting, narrow-gauged passage. At this stage, ignorance of the distal gauge proved blissful.

In addition, night sight clearly was helping reduce the tunnel's torment, because without it, groping along in utter darkness would have been claustrophobic and unbearable it seemed to Barnes. God had blessed him and he knew it. He could see what others could not. *TIBIA.*

For the most part, Barnes' progress went unimpeded until he transitioned from being hunched over, then on all fours, and finally to a belly crawl. The only impediment, other than being terrorized by the whole underground experience, was the dangling rope strand trailing from his bound hands extended. On occasion it would drag in the dirt and get pinned under foot or under body, resulting in an unnerving jerk or tight squeeze—step-by-step to foot-by-foot to inch-by-inch—being slender turned out to be a plus.

The journey continued until farther down the passageway when a faint flicker reflected off the moisture-soaked walls of a more recently carved-out corridor. At last he could stand up enough to stretch his back.

When Barnes reached the first room-sized cavity, probably the living quarters for the medical staff, he saw ahead that Claire's stretcher was being lowered through a trap door to another level—deeper down. Fortunately the immobilization straps they had used to secure her for the evacuation flight had been reapplied and effectively tightened to provide better maneuverability in the tricky twists and turns of the tunnel.

Finally, it was Barnes' turn to go into the laddered hole. He negotiated his body backward through the trap door, hands positioned in front on the rungs. Over his shoulder as he descended he could see that the shaft emptied into an elongated, arched chamber. Claire was there, her stretcher now resting on two makeshift sawhorses. The hand-scooped earth and hammer-chiseled rock walls were slimy and damp. Not the conditions one would choose for an operating suite, but obviously it was adequate by the standards of war—and those standards would have to do.

The topside source of power, a sputtering generator, was causing a fluctuating intensity of illumination in the room. Using a handheld flashlight, the Swedish nurses were working as a team taking vital signs from Claire Marshall. These women both spoke fluent English. Though significant political and ideological differences probably existed between these nurses and the American doctor, Barnes was more than thankful for their presence under the circumstances.

Bindings removed, Barnes was handed the flashlight. Claire's right pupil was dilated; however, it was not fixed but definitely sluggish to the flashlight beam. Her pulse rate was under sixty; blood pressure splits showed systolic: rising and diastolic: falling; and her breathing was getting slower and deeper. She was now unresponsive to the applied pain of pressing her sternum and pinching her neck and calf muscles. This complex of signs established that she had drifted into a coma. Barnes was deeply concerned that these could be precursors heralding a herniation into the brain stem area. The clock was ticking its final seconds, but this was not the end of some game. Imminently, it could be the end of a life.

From the moment of their capture, the decision to save or let die, (which Barnes had dreaded—hoping to avoid but knowing it was inevitable) now lay before him in the person of someone whom he loved. Unknowing and unconscious, she held the key to his heart. The one person, it would seem, who could have helped him unlock the intricacies of intimacy that had been sealed since the death of his brother, was herself surrendering life right before his very eyes. Barnes churned with anger, crushed by a feeling of helplessness—again!

Stop. Did not the paramount question involve more than just his own self-pitying emotions, Barnes thought. Did he love Claire enough to let her die in peace? She was in a coma—dead to this world while awaiting the world to come. She was not suffering. In her unconscious state she was oblivious to a world of war, a world where the innocent suffer for no fault of their own. She was already free in the spirit. Did his <u>more</u> love for her supersede his choosing to let her go to the One who loved her *most?*

A woman's whispering voice invaded the stillness. Barnes thought it was Claire. He leaned closer. It was not.

One of the nurses had softly uttered, "What are you going to do?" Reality had returned; the emergency of the moment remained.

The differential of neurological diagnoses boggled Barnes' mind. However, he methodically reasoned, if the bleeding inside her head was epidural and it was complicating an existing subdural hematoma (a clot from the previous head trauma) with increased pressure, then the treatment decision was clear: *an emergency evacuation of the skull was required!* That was the medical choice, but what about the emotional one? Were his caring and his compassion for Claire clouding his concentration for functioning as a physician? And even further, what about the spiritual argument? Just let her die!

In the far away fringes of the medical mind of a pediatrician freshly arrived from an internship, specific neurosurgical techniques had been stored to *accumulate dust*. For Barnes, experiential operating room exposure to head trauma cases had been nonexistent. Pictorial and diagrammatical remembrances from textbook accounts would have to assist his common-sense reasoning. A practical understanding of general procedures in surgery would have to suffice. The ancient adage, "I treated; God healed," kept the situation fluidly in perspective. Barnes had a principle that dovetailed with it. Since medical school he had always believed and competitively practiced the principle of *"never conceding the battle for life except into the hands of God."* The final decision was made. Barnes was not ready to concede that battle yet for Claire. "Lord, please help us. Thy will be done. *TIBIA!"*

The battalion surgeon would play the odds and drill burr holes into the right temporal region of the skull first. But with what medical instruments? What tools and equipment would he find in this underworld hospital? In short and simple statements Barnes inquired of the two nurses what general anesthesia was available, if any; and did they have anything with which he could put holes in the skull. One, named Greta, brought over a can of ether with a mask; and the younger nurse, Inger, scrounged up what appeared to be a hand-operated auger drill. Barnes truly was back in the Dark Ages of medicine, in more ways than one. "Maybe even further back," he mused with a hint of humor. "During the *Stone Age* where primitive hospitals existed as hollowed-out houses of horror." With this brief mental distraction over, his anger slightly allayed, Barnes returned his focus to the criticality of *his* situation—or more significantly, Claire's.

Proper preparation for surgery demanded that Claire's hair would have to be cut, a tragedy in itself. First, her golden locks were shorn, blood-stained clumps tumbling down onto the slimy, mud floor after each snip of the scissor blades. Finally, her scalp was shaved, then lathered with bar soap, and sponge-bathed with an alcohol solution. Wrapping on an undersized surgical slicker, Barnes rolled its sleeves to above his elbows. He then scrubbed up with soap and copiously drenched his hands with alcohol—no gloves—so much for sterile technique under the circumstances. Disinfection was totally in God's hands.

Improvising, Claire's head was partially immobilized using field boots, wrapped in surgical towels, and adhesive tape to simulate a rigid neck collar. Positioning her skull to the left to expose the right temporal region, her head was then draped and fixed down with bandage strips taped to stretcher handles. This approach left a poor exposure to the surgical field, but was adequate, absent a true operating table.

These two nurses exhibited an air of confidence and professionalism that impressed Barnes. They anticipated the needs of the operator and moved within the narrow spaces without collision in the manner of ballerinas who were intimately familiar with every inch of their dance floor. They conversed between themselves with hand signals scarcely conspicuous to Barnes. Prep complete, Inger donned a cleaner scrub smock and took an assisting position to the right of Barnes on the same side of the cot. Greta administered the general anesthesia by drip; and after a final monitor of Claire's vital signs, she confirmed that the patient was ready, or as ready as she could be.

The only distraction at that point was internal—that nagging and pressing of urgency. Everyone surrounding that cot recognized that time was running out. The hourglass of life with its steady trickle of sand was precariously in need of an inverting.

Scalpel in hand, Barnes made a four inch incision. "Lord, help me. *TIBIA*." A scalp flap of skin was dissected down to the bone and raised. He proceeded quickly and surely beyond his level of technical skill. His assistant was proactively facilitating every action. Maximizing every exposure, decisively passing instruments, and effectively clamping all serious bleeders. (Blood loss would be the primary danger with its concomitant shock, anoxia, and cardiac arrest.)

The next stage was to drill at a slight angle through the temporal bone and the fibrous dura sheet which encapsulated the brain. If the hematoma or hemorrhaging was taking place in the epidural or the subdural spaces, this procedure of perforating the skull would allow drainage, and thus reduce the pressure on the brain.

Before every turn of the sprocket wheel, Barnes silently prayed, "Help me, Lord." With one final, delicate crank of the handle, he tactilely sensed the skull had been penetrated. He froze. No reaction from the patient. Only dark blood oozed from the hole. It was quickly swabbed away repeatedly by Greta as it drained across the shaven temple and seeped behind the patient's ears.

Barnes glanced at the "anesthetist" receiving a thumbs-up. No words were spoken. Claire was tolerating the procedure well.

("Thank you, Lord!") Her blood pressure was stabilizing and her pulse rate was coming up ever so slowly. Only the precious healing commodity, time, would tell if this decompression was life-saving.

What to do next? That defined the burning question bouncing back and forth in Barnes' subconscious. The alternatives being mentally processed were only slightly being perceived considering his numbed state. He knew that Claire would need more definitive treatment in an American medical facility as soon as possible; but how could he get a dust-off mission to this location controlled by the enemy? Immediate answers and solutions were not forthcoming. The only certitude: Claire Marshall could not be moved, *period!* No transfer to a recovery room, no treatment in an Intensive Care Unit.

Along with the two Swedish caregivers, Barnes assumed the role of a critical care nurse attentively overseeing Claire's postoperative condition: checking blood pressures, pulses, respirations and temperatures. The three attendings rotated in shifts.

Generator time exhausted, the room's only source of light became a few candles, strategically placed for optimum illumination of the enclosure. When the flames died out, there was the flashlight, but to conserve the batteries, it was turned on only to aid in the examination of Claire. The physician prisoner and his patient, the doctor and his friend, would have to wait out the night hours imprisoned, not by chains, but by total darkness. Sheltered by a sanctuary in stone, a refuge in rock, they were trapped below ground in a candlelit catacomb while up above, under the stars, the war went on.

Barnes crouched into a corner crevice at arm's length from Claire's cot, listening to her every breath like a mother, stationed crib side, monitoring each and every movement of a sick child. Fatigue forced him to doze fitfully, but physical discomfort would startle him back awake. As he watched his assistants, Greta and Inger, carry out their duties, he puzzled over why they were here, so far from home—in a war zone—in the border boondocks of Cambodia. He posited reasons for administering medical care to North Vietnamese soldiers as either mercenary or humanitarian. The arrived at conclusion: their goal was simply to help alleviate the pain and suffering of war wherever they found it. Not surprisingly, they had found it in Southeast Asia beneath the battlefields of the Fishhook.

As true pacifists, these two women had not chosen a side for right or for wrong in the Vietnam War. Their activities offered no propaganda machinations for either side. By opposing any use of force for any reason in any circumstance, their hatred for physical hostility was established in every fiber of their character. Summarized simply, they hated war! Like those who commit their lives to a religious order, these women had taken solemn vows to provide for the welfare of all human beings, even in the midst of warfare. What Barnes discerned in a very short time was that their neutrality was genuine—and so too their demonstrated compassion.

Anti-war protestors in America conveyed a different image. It saddened Barnes that in wartime his anti-war countrymen would choose sides against their own—even the side of a brutal enemy—while claiming to be anti-war. Barnes believed that anti-war should literally mean anti-war. Arbitrarily choosing which wars were just and unjust, which wars should be supported or condemned, seemed to dilute and defeat the meaning of the designation.

These Swedish nurses had figured it out and were comfortable in the happy medium they had found—"If you need medical help, we will provide it, no matter on which side you stand or fight." (Such behavior reminded Barnes of his great grandfather during the Civil War between the States.) The indicting lesson to be learned by American anti-war protestors from the attitudes of wartime providers of medical care was, when a state of war exists between two powers, if an individual is *not truly neutral* regarding the two, that person strangely becomes an advocate, inclined to aiding and abetting one side against the other. Propaganda as a weapon system is neutralized when one is truly *anti-war*.

From his growing edge Barnes would concur with the following premise: a person who <u>hates</u> war and is consistent in condemning all sides in the conflict, assigning no fault to either, is worthy of respect even if the respecter is not, in that particular situation, in agreement with the one who hates. Captain Adam Barnes respected these two women from neutral Sweden. As angels of mercy they had chosen no sides—only God's.

CHAPTER 31

TRADE TALKS: A LIFE FOR A LIFE

Military activities in the camp came early, before daybreak. Through the bountiful jungle bamboo shoots, only Venus, the morning star, was visible in the eastern sky as Barnes surfaced from his night in the underworld. What little sleep he got had been restless. He awoke with a common affliction for him, an adrenalin-withdrawal headache. He was nauseated from lack of food and from breathing the stale air of the mine pit.

U.S. Army Captain Adam Barnes was escorted to the commanding officer at the headquarter's hooch. Colonel Ming Tau, head of the North Vietnamese forces in that Cambodian province, sat behind a small wooden table upon which lay a holstered pistol, probably retrieved from the helicopter crash site. There was nothing remarkable about his appearance, though his uniform was the only one heavily starched.

Barnes offered the prerequisite name, rank, and serial number. But then, without interruption as he had done with Major Thieu, he blurted firmly the request that the non-combatant nurse be taken back to Vietnam for further medical care.

The commander snapped erect from his chair. With both

hands he pounded his fists down on the table. The force flipped the gun to the floor. Aggressively leaning toward Barnes, he harangued the captured captain emphatically that the ongoing offensive by his "invading imperialist" friends precluded any prisoner transfer. It was out of the question. If she were to survive the next few days, she would be taken north to Hanoi and turned over to the Red Cross. (This was the equivalent to a death march in Barnes' mind. Claire would never survive such a trip.) Thieu was present for this interrogation session, but being just a liaison for the Viet Cong, he said nothing.

Convalescence for Claire to travel the reverse on the rugged infiltration trails would take more than just a few days. Her recovery in and of itself would be gradual and fraught with serious complications like infection. It would take a miracle. Even though Greta and Inger were most conscientious in their care of their missionary counterpart, the underground environment was not conducive to regaining one's health and strength. The difficulty of moving her to the outside would be compounded by the labyrinthine network of passages they would have to negotiate. Once moved above ground into an open air structure, she would need additional surgery, antibiotics and more intensive nursing care—treatment she required *yesterday!* All things considered, the outcome for Claire looked bleak.

On the other hand, the fresh and open air were breathing new life into Barnes. His headache was easing; however, his hunger was not. And his sense of freedom was only as fleeting as a rare cooling breeze in a tidal wave of heat. In this enemy compound a prisoner of war like Barnes would have to be confined. He expected a bamboo cage and he got it, an enclosure measuring five feet long, two feet wide and four feet high. This bamboo-barred box was stowed in a peculiar place, wedged beneath the residence hooch of the NVA commander.

The ceiling of Barnes' cell cage was the bamboo floor of Ming's hut. The flooring was composed of entwined strips of wood and slats of bamboo, gapped apart for ventilation and drainage. Based on the smell it was obvious that this functioned more often as a holding pen for farm animals than it did as a cell for captured combatants.

The starched uniform tipped Barnes off that this camp commandant was one of the privileged NVA officers. (Barnes always was impressed with how sharply his own uniform shirts looked after being cleaned by the local laundry woman. Colonel Ming had brought his family with him: a wife (his "laundress") and two teenage sons, probably fourteen and twelve.

Their household furnishings were quite austere: one table, a few chairs, woven sleeping mats, a bucket for water, and several rice bowls. During the day the wife cooked and cleaned; the boys trained and studied. In the home, an oriental formality governed socially; outside the hutch, military discipline permeated every aspect of family life. The expression of emotion was the exception. On the rare occasion when passion was displayed, it was related to the war and the keen dislike for American soldiers with whom they were fighting.

The responsibility for overseeing prisoner Barnes in the cage fell to the eldest son: the ration of a rice bowl per day and the hydration of one daily cup of water. Taunting recitations from the young man were minimal.

"American GI, go home. You will lose like the French. Leave Vietnam alone."

This jail keeper was growing up too early and too fast. The

assigned stints as a litter bearer in the underground hospital had made the boy aware of the realities and ravages of war. Wounded and severely maimed soldiers regularly passed through the facility on their way back up the Ho Chi Minh trail for rehabilitation in the North. Most of the injured never made it from the field.

Over the next few days the only other English-speaking contact for Barnes with the enemy happened to be Major Thieu. He was not the best interpreter, language to language, but was a valuable interpreter of the ongoing activities in the camp. With his freedom of movement as an officer, he represented the only source of information about the condition of Claire since Barnes had been separated from his patient. In solitude, Barnes' thoughts were flooded with questions about her. "Was she conscious? Any fever? Was she aware of her circumstances? Would Thieu help her get back to South Vietnam—at least to the orphanage at Nui Ba Dinh?"

Major Thieu's attempts at answering the wave upon wave of inquiries were painfully inadequate. His broken-English responses raised more questions than his words answered. When the intensity of Barnes' frustration aggravated Thieu too much, the Cong leader would just turn and walk away.

Life in the cage was a tormenting annoyance in the mind. The only true respite came in the solace of prayer; prayer for Claire, prayer for wisdom and self-control, and prayer for courage as a prisoner of war. "Lord, please help me, sinner that I am..." and stroking with his hand the length of his shin bone, "*TIBIA.*" Barnes needed some kind of plan, some way to escape, some opportunity to get Claire Marshall out of captivity and into an evacuation hospital. Impossible dreams it would seem.

In any case, on the third day such an opportunity did present itself. Just before dawn a commotion of running feet on the floor above his cell awakened Barnes. The only word he could pick up that sounded familiar was *"dau,"* the Vietnamese word for pain. The twelve-year-old son apparently was suffering severe abdominal cramps. Barnes recognized the symptoms of an acutely ill child.

The boy lay reclined on his floor mat just above Barnes— guarded, doubled up, and motionless. His mother knelt quietly beside him, but he was preventing anyone from touching his body. Words exchanged between the two of them were few. An occasional query from the mama-san must have been, *"No bi dau?"* Where does it hurt?

The fourteen-year-old had been sent to fetch his father from the command center, and those were the running footsteps which had roused Barnes from his intermittent slumbering. Within minutes Colonel Ming strode with deliberation toward the hut, the older child proudly mimicking his every step as a dutiful soldier might trail after an inspecting general. Behind the bamboo curtain which divided sleeping quarters from the kitchen, the conversation between the colonel and his wife was brief; then the father left. The older teen remained, standing by the front entranceway as if on guard. There would be no breakfast for Barnes that morning.

When late morning sunbeams finally broke through the over growth to bathe the cage-end of the hooch, Barnes saw the youngest boy flex his right thigh tighter against his stomach, replicating the fetal position. Through a crack in the floor, the child's face was visible. Only his posture confirmed the pain. He uttered not a word of complaint—not a sound, not a moan. This episode had now continued beyond three to four hours by

Barnes' recollection when, after a muffled heaving sound, vomitus and bile came dripping through the slotted spaces in the floor. Evidence of an acute abdomen? Barnes believed it could be. No doubt, this boy was seriously ill.

As a physician, Barnes was instinctively formulating a differential diagnosis in his head: bacterial or parasitic infection of the urinary or gastrointestinal tract, acute hepatitis, doubtful some kind of stone, more probably an inflamed appendix. Christian compassion tugged at his heartstrings drawing him toward wanting to help. Hunger and thirst voted for vindictive non-involvement. A whole new meaning of the phrase, tug-of-war, was evolving. Was it not anger that was sustaining him in the cramped quarters of the inhumane box? Or was it something else?

Midday or early afternoon, Major Thieu could be seen walking out of the compound toward the cage. He had an NVA regular accompanying him. The subordinate soldier had been instructed to unlock the cage and to remove the U.S. captain, bringing him to Colonel Ming's headquarters. The three men in single file, Thieu, Barnes and the armed guard respectively marched through the village to the TOC of the North Vietnamese.

Once inside the fortified bunker, Barnes stood before the desk of Colonel Ming Tau. The colonel and the Viet Cong major began conversing privately off to the right in the shadows, the only light source being a single bulb suspended over the desk. Shortly, Thieu stepped to attention adjacent to Barnes. The colonel entered the halo of the light and began to speak. Major Thieu translated word for word into English the best he could—butchering the grammar and some pronunciations but, for the most part, intelligible enough for Barnes to understand the gist of what was being said.

The initial remarks only confirmed what Barnes had surmised from his prison-cell vantage point. The colonel's son was critically sick and this commander was ordering Barnes to examine and treat him. The parenthetical phrase "or else" embodied the threatening consequences of bodily harm and a return to the cage if the command was not carried out as demanded. The obligatory drama by the parent failed to intimidate an already irate Barnes, still boiling over from the commandant's obstinate stand taken in regard to Claire. As a prisoner of war, this demand in Barnes' mind, represented a bargaining chip, if not for himself, possibly for Claire.

Standing chest-to-face with the NVA colonel, the barefoot Barnes stretched erect and reiterated his name, rank, and serial number. That response, of course, enraged his adversary who stamped his boot down on Barnes' toes and struck him a backhand blow to the cheek as the doctor bent forward in reflex to the initial stomp. All Barnes could think was, "No retaliation. No retaliation or you're dead!" The aggressor then turned to his Cong comrade, Major Thieu, and ordered him to state the original command again. Before the verbal translation was completed, Barnes interrupted the halting flow of words with a wave off by his hand.

Wiping a stream of blood from his nose with the opposite palm, he began the restatement of his identification items but concluded with one conditional addition. "If you will let the missionary nurse be taken back to her orphanage at Nui Ba Dinh *immediately*, I will examine and treat your son."

Thieu interpreted this response.

Barnes felt confident that the NVA would not release Claire to the advancing American Army. As a hostage she seemed as a more valuable bargaining chip for the North—if she lived (and Ming thought she was going to die anyway). Alternately in the back of his mind, Barnes was counting on the fact that one battery of the 1st/30th Artillery might be back on the mountain, and they could get Claire MEDEVACed out—if only she could get there alive.

The plan mentally improvised by Barnes had a critical timetable. Being a pediatrician without any significant surgical experience, if he could assure the freedom of his close friend in advance of his anticipated operating on this child, she could be behind the lines and out of harm's way no matter how successful he was as a surgeon. Major Thieu, with his connections in the Viet Cong and his intimate knowledge of the network of infiltration routes across Binh Long province in the Fishhook, could get her safely to the mountain mission. Surely he would do it since Claire had done so much for his Montagnard people. She was not an enemy and he had to know that. Behind his snarling demeanor, Barnes believed, flowed an untapped fountain of goodness. But would Thieu do it? Would he risk his own demise or capture in order to save an American, one barely clinging to life, who realistically should not survive the trip?

As Barnes reviewed all his options in that momentary pause in the negotiations, the enemy stood stern. He backed around behind his desk, maintaining eye contact with his captured quarry every step of the way. From that position of power, like a judge behind his bench, he bellowed in a most emphatic manner, "No!" Barnes did not need an interpreter for such a terse retort to his proposed concession. Instantly, Ming ordered Barnes be returned to the bamboo box without food or water. The colonel had called the captain's bluff to save Claire.

On the roadway back, Barnes passed by the front side of the living quarters under which his cell cage was attached. The strap-hinged shutters were propped open to where he could see the sick boy balled up on the hut floor. By now Barnes was highly suspicious that this young child was suffering from an acute appendicitis. In such cases the appendix could rupture, causing a peritonitis and possibly the formation of an abscess. Without treatment this boy could die! Seeing a truly sick kid may not affect the conscience of a social culture that seemingly has no reverence for life, but it would impact the conscience of one who called himself a Christian. "Lord, forgive me, sinner that I am."

Barnes stepped toward Major Thieu.

"I know you will do the right thing for the nurse."

Then Barnes spoke in a whisper, distinctly and slowly, "Tell Ming that I will do what he wants. I will care for his son."

CHAPTER 32

A SURGICAL SHOT
IN THE DARK

I t took only a short time for the message from Captain Barnes to be relayed to Colonel Ming. Reaction followed swiftly. As Barnes was escorted back to the residential hut, outside a strange air of quiet foreboding existed. No distant pops of artillery firing or "whomps" of exploding shells could be heard. The doctor could take advantage of the calm to examine the sick boy, whose obvious discomfort was made apparent by his fidgety posturing on the floor to relieve the painful paroxysms.

Barnes gently rotated the twelve-year-old onto his back. He felt his forehead which was only slightly warm; but the boy had a truly toxic facies. Cautiously, Barnes palpated the abdomen, first on the left and then the right, intentionally avoiding the right lower quadrant initially. As he moved his palm and fingers, delicately probing deeper into the abdominal cavity, he kept his eyes glued on the face of the child. The boy made no utterances, but muscle rigidity was detected beneath the fingertips. The boy's facial expression changed dramatically when Barnes pressed deeper into the stomach space and withdrew his hand suddenly. The rapid release of the examining pressure created the telltale sign of rebound tenderness. The boy abruptly sat up in a reflex spasm associated with peritoneal irritation. Reliability of Barnes' initial diagnosis was corroborated. He was dealing with an acute abdomen—rule out appendicitis.

Now came the hard part. How would Barnes describe what treatment was at this point an urgent necessity? Speaking slowly, repeating phrases, and using simple hand gestures, he detailed the medical dilemma to Major Thieu, who interpreted to his NVA superior, Ming. The son would need surgery—exploratory surgery to check for and treat a life-threatening problem. Removal of the appendix was probable. Barnes struggled to resolve how much technical information was too much information in this setting. How do you explain the need for "the knife" in Vietnamese? Ming would have to trust his enemy to save his son.

A bugle alert broke up these deliberative discussions. Immediate circumstances would force Ming Tau as a father and as a soldier to make quick command decisions regarding his family member and his military men. Already everyone in the village was scampering to the tunnel entrance, like a colony of ants when their mound has been disturbed. A silencing of the sounds of war often signaled "by telegraph" a pending U.S. Air Force bombardment. Coupled with the disengagement of American infantry patrols along the border and the no-fly clearing of the horizon, the North Vietnamese knew a bombing run was about to commence. In multiple episodes before, they had withstood similar aerial attacks by simply retreating to the sanctity of the tunnels, knowing that only a direct hit could cause any significant damage.

Major Thieu reacted first after a nod of consent from Colonel Ming who sprinted off the hut porch toward the TOC. The son was loaded into a hammock-like sling and carried by pole down the excavated trench to the main tunnel. Guards diverted Barnes again over toward the spider-hole entrance, deep into the inner sanctum caves, and farther below to the level of the hospital core. Using the alternate entry for a second time was in all probability a security measure against escape Barnes reasoned.

Transiting the tunnel, Barnes detected the cadenced hum of a gas-powered motor. On that first day underground, fear had distorted or blocked the hearing of almost every auditory undertone. On this trip, variations in volume of the rhythmic running of a generator were consistently distinguished in the background, the sound diminishing with each level of his descent—loudest at the entrance and faint in the inner hospital, but always audible to some extent if listened for.

The operating area seemed more dimly lit than before with the beam intensity still varying irregularly. Yet the lighting was adequate enough for Barnes to use his gift. The owl swiveled his head as he entered the chamber from above, searching and hoping for a glimpse of Claire before the bombing started. The physician was the one being closely monitored, not the patient.

Claire was still in the recovery area, a domed alcove carved into the stone at the far end of the room. She was lying on her side strapped to the cot in what visually to anyone else was a darkened tomb. Barnes could see through the shadows. She was being attended by one of the nurses. Just as Barnes stepped toward the semicircular vault, the bombing began.

Though the B-52 bombers themselves could not be heard in the caves, the carpet detonation patterns resounding from above ground confirmed an "arc-light" run was in progress. The earth trembled with each series of staccato impactions and so did Barnes. He crouched with his back and shoulders arched as if to hold up the earthen shelf under which he hunched. With each concussive whomp, the ceiling released a shower of dirt and dust down upon the occupants of that chamber. Breathing was impaired and the T-shirt which Barnes wore served as a makeshift face mask. Above, the terrain was taking a terrible beating; but those in the tunnel complex would survive another air assault.

During a lull and because of the resultant atmosphere of floating dust, Major Thieu moved Claire Marshall down another passageway by utilizing the hammock-like litter and pole used to transport Colonel Ming's son. "Pallbearers" under Thieu's command conveyed her comatose body delicately through the labyrinth of carved-out corridors. Barnes was directed to stay there in the space cored out for the purpose of surgical operations. Both Inger and Greta were in the corner scrubbing up in a wash basin. They would assist again.

After a brief strategy session with the surgical sisters, Barnes placed his hand on the boy's forehead, attempted a reassuring smile, and offered a silent prayer. The child felt more febrile. Had perforation occurred? Blanket wraps were adapted to anchor the patient's arms to his side and his legs to the cot. As Barnes began his soap scrub, the nurses prepped the young boy by swabbing his whole abdominal surface with alcohol. A few breaths into the mask and the lad was unconscious.

The system of lighting for surgical procedures underground was in and of itself a wiring phenomenon. A bunker-protected generator above ground supplied electric current through strands of cord which were threaded through the corridors without benefit of conduit tubes or troughs to protect them. The wire lines terminated in the operating complex, with a single light bulb in the center of the chamber cavity. The anesthetized patient's cot was positioned so that the strongest beam bathed the abdominal region as one focal projection of light. The lamp just hung suspended from the roof. It could not be directed to improve angles of illumination.

Barnes primary concern was not related to whether he had enough lighting, but to whether he had enough learning to perform an appendectomy under these conditions. This would be his first attempt at abdominal surgery. The full extent of his experience amounted to one observation. The scalpel had never been in his hand for such a surgical procedure. His mind was being overwhelmed with doubt. "What if the operation goes badly and the boy dies? What if the operation goes well and he still dies? Perforation, massive peritonitis, shock, abscess formation?" Tension mounting!

It would seem that doubt and anxiety were undermining his ability to remember basic anatomy—to envision the tissue layers through which his knife would have to pass. "Four layers, four cuts." The four incision method was named the "Gridiron" effect. Barnes tried to imagine the metal grate on a barbecue grill or the crosshatched lines of a football field. An illustrated diagram in his head outlining the procedure could walk him through the surgery step by step. "Four layers, four cuts, *gridiron*." The moment an anatomical sketch would flash on the screen of his mind, the image would start to fade away like interference distorting a television transmission. Four layers, four cuts, *gridiron*. Visualization of an action in advance of its performance had always augmented muscle memory for Barnes in sports. He was trying to apply that technique here, but with little success. More stress!

Barnes returned to focusing on the anatomy. He imagined he was drawing an explanatory picture for a patient. It worked. He saw the four layers of the right lower quadrant: the skin/fat, the fibrous fascia, the sheets of muscle, and the peritoneum. That was the order—to open and in reverse to close. Barnes knew it would take total concentration to differentiate these four tissue divisions distinctly, especially with the expected camouflage of flowing blood. Four layers, four cuts, gridiron. It was game time. "*Lord, help...TIBIA.*"

The initial incision was made long, about six inches, for exploratory purposes if needed. Cosmetics would not be an issue. The vertical cut bisecting the layer of skin and subcutaneous fat (almost non-existent) of the right lower quadrant was quickly separated into flaps with blunt-edged scissors. Retractors were inserted to expose layer two. The second incision ran horizontally through the fascia—minimal bleeding. Along the lateral margin of the rectus abdominus muscle a third cut was extended vertically, parallel to the first skin incised line, but Barnes went too deep and pricked a hole in the peritoneal lining ahead of schedule. He had entered the abdominal cavity and did not know if such an inadvertent act warranted a "whoops!" "No harm, no foul," he thought. Bleeders tied, and blood loss kept to a minimum, Barnes proceeded to enlarge the hole in the peritoneum, stretching it obliquely with a retractor. This completed the Gridiron effect. Four layers, four cuts.

Standing in an underground cave and reaching into the abdominal cavity of the patient, Barnes searched for the appendix. And there it was, right where it was supposed to be ("Thank God"). Barnes breathed a sigh of relief. This troublesome little appendage to the gut was enlarged and inflamed, but not ruptured ("Thank God!").

Barnes cupped the cecum and its attached appendix cautiously in his hands to get a better viewing angle in the limited light. The unusual bulges in the bowel's cul-de-sac caused him to wonder if a tiny invader like a pinworm might have instigated this pathologic crisis. Taking up residence in this blind pouch, a parasite would trigger a systemic alarm to marshal the cellular scouts and skirmishers of inflammation. This foreign infestation from the "North" being confined, the boy's body would respond with an all-out declaration of war against the worm. It was too early to judge who would eventually win—the warring worm or the warrior waif.

Disrupting this inner supposing, not to mention the outer quieting of the moment, another wave of saturation bombing commenced. There were earth quaking tremors. The rocks rumbled and roared. It was like being caught in the center of a severe thunderstorm surrounded by multiple strikes of lightning, each bolt pounding powerfully against the ground. Only in this case, the location was the underground. Then, too close! *Boom!*

Instantly, a blackout. That seismic detonation hitting directly overhead plunged the cave into darkness. Even though the mechanical droning produced by the generator could still be heard, re-illumination was not instantly forthcoming. The blast must have dislodged the cable at the terminal source or severed it somewhere along the line. Barnes did not know which. *Nobody* dared move. Inger quickly groped to place a towel drape over the incision site, startling Barnes whose hands were still in the abdominal cavity holding a segment of bowel. His physical frame was frozen in place. Without a source of light, what *could* they do? What *would* they do?

Total darkness was creating an awesome and somewhat terrifying sensory deprivation experience. Yet unperturbed, Inger stepped back from the operating table and lit a match which she had stashed in her pocket just for this eventuality—and for lighting her cigarettes. Obviously this did not represent the inaugural interruption of electricity for this camp. It was a frequent occurrence for a variety of reasons. But for the first timer, just more pressure!

Without panic, Greta fumbled a search for the OR flashlight she had been using to take vital signs and monitor her patient's status. When her fingers found it and pressed the switch, the resultant beam which came on was now very weak. The batteries were dying and replacements were not available. So, with a second match a candle was lit—then several more. Visibility somewhat restored, Inger asked Barnes if he could see well enough to continue the operation.

Since his visual acuity was enhanced in his right eye by dim light, Barnes acknowledged that they would proceed. What complicated the situation for him was not the lack of adequate lighting, but rather the unequal accommodation factors associated with having night vision in only one eye. This limited his ability to make precise distinctions between specific tissue types, skin, fascia, muscle, peritoneum, for the process of wound closure. Some significant blood vessels would also need to be differentiated for tying off. He would be trusting his sense of touch as well as his sense of sight. If he wanted to prevent the process from being slowed up considerably, he would also have to trust Inger. Two sets of eyes would have to be better than one.

Firsthand experience had taught Barnes that dependence on seeing with only one eye—the other, closed shut—did alter his depth perception in his central field of vision. If both his eyes were open and attempting to focus under dimly lit conditions, he had discovered that a certain clarity of image would be sacrificed. (Choosing pediatrics was partially predicated by Barnes' optical disability. Less than perfect eyesight discouraged the pursuit of a practice in general surgery where keen vision was almost a prerequisite.)

At this point in the procedure, Barnes turned to address Nurse Inger and confessed that he was having trouble telling what was what tissue-wise. He encouraged her to be aggressive in clearing blood and clots from the field—and to stop him if he was about to cut the wrong thing or suture the wrong incision margin back together. She nodded in acknowledgement.

Ever so gently, Barnes lifted the proximal end of the large intestine up and out, resting it on the now moistened drape towel. His desired goal: easy access to the appendix per se. The appendicular artery and vein were quickly identified, separated, and ligated. The next step was to tie off that angry-looking worm (vermiform appendix) at its exposed junction with the bowel pouch. The three-inch-long appendage was severed between the ties, and with a purse-string suture, the stump was buried into the lumen of the large intestine. When the stump was satisfactorily inverted, the suture was pulled snug and tied. Now, find four layers; suture four cuts. And close. End result: *an iron grid.* At this point in the procedure, beneath the surgeon's slicker, Barnes was raining perspiration. Noting his drenched T-shirt as the coat was removed, Nurse Greta handed Barnes a ladle of water. He dropped to one knee having no idea how dehydrated he had become.

In retrospect, the operating technique of the surgeon was far from textbook in quality and in technical skill; but Colonel Ming's son now had a chance. However, Barnes knew that without antibiotics, namely penicillin, this child would surely experience complications—serious, life-threatening complications.

"Lord, another one 'into your hands'… TIBIA."

CHAPTER 33

ONE LAST HOPE FOR RECOVERY

After the timed tempest of the air strike came stillness—an abrupt and eerie calm—as when the warring elements of a thunderstorm conclude their atmospheric chaos and pass on. "At last!" Steady sprinklings of dirt from the crusted ceiling had settled as a new stratum on the pasty floor. Everything which inhabited the chamber cave was coated with dust as if painted with a ghastly color of grayish pale. Ashen faces appeared as dead in the wavering candlelight. The final bombardment had ceased. Final was always a guess, but never a guarantee for either side.

Barnes was discussing with the women a decision about taking the boy up to the surface to recover in the nurses' hut, as soon as he could be moved. His rehabilitation would require some ambulatory activity before the day was over, surgery in the morning; up walking by the night, and such could not be achieved underground in the dark. The recuperative powers of the human body, especially in the young, were a recurring amazement to Barnes—for man truly was "fearfully and wonderfully made." (Ps. 139:14)

As a part of his evolving plan, Barnes discerned intuitively that this would be an advantageous time to transfer Claire above ground too. She occupied critical treatment space in the field hospital that might soon be needed for wounded NVA soldiers. This added incentive to move her from underground could be influential to Colonel Ming's thinking. It was hoped that his command opposition might have softened by the recent events. In favor of combat readiness, his consent might be forthcoming. Undoubtedly, it was worth broaching the subject to the colonel through Major Thieu. What did Barnes have to lose by asking?

A second inducement favoring an affirmative response from Ming revolved around the willingness of the nurses to provide care for both patients out of the way of trauma traffic in one location—their bunkered hospital hut on the edge of the village. Unbeknownst to Barnes until now, this recovery ward was linked to the underground surgery center by its own gateway to the underworld, a separate subterranean network of mined-out passageways.

Captain Barnes, restored to prisoner status, was commandeered to help lift the son's stretcher and transport him out. Just as the cot was elevated off the frames which served as its support, the light bulb, hanging at the tall physician's eye level, flashed on. The sudden brilliance momentarily blinded Barnes. The glare caused him to stagger with his end of the load, slipping to his knees on the slimed surface of mud. The boy slid down the "slide" toward Barnes but stayed on the canvas because of the wrapped bindings. Just a jostling, nothing more Barnes hoped.

It took several minutes for the spots in Barnes' visual field to dissipate and for his eyes to adapt to the dark environment again with his special night scope acuity.

Along the narrow, lighted corridors through which Barnes

had never coursed, the grade angled down rather than up. Constant air currents caressed his neck and ears. The draft flowed in the direction in which they were progressing. This natural ventilation system whistled like what one would expect to hear in a wind tunnel, which it functionally was. Doorway intersections led into room-shaped dead ends, the interiors of which were visible only to Barnes. These caves were all unoccupied, though some of them stored piles of supply crates.

Another twenty yards and the passageway opened into a chasm-like chamber, twenty feet across. The ceiling was a domed-shaped expanse of solid rock. A huge vertical vent hole pierced the dome like a mine shaft. It was an eight-foot-square silo lined with ladders on all four sides.

Portable wooden risers were packed flush against the side walls of the chamber, potential seats or steps to the lowest rungs of the ladders. For the first time, Barnes could stand erect to his full height without bending at the waist. After the bearers placed the stretcher on the floor, Barnes experienced immediate relief from lower back strain associated with bending and bowing, stooping, and hunching down in the tunnel passageways. Full body stretching eased his muscular spasms. The cramping discomfort from dehydration was momentarily alleviated as Barnes sat on the platformed bench massaging his calves. Fatigue found a weakness and rushed in only to be repelled by a guard's gesture to get moving.

Above him, the shaft rose up about two stories (somewhere between 30 and 40 feet). Barnes could detect the outlines of a makeshift lift suspended from above and descending down the core. It was comprised of a double block-and-tackle system and a wooden, spindle winch. Functionally it appeared rigged for hoisting cargo, hammock slings, or hospital litters. The accompanying soldiers were already securing the four stretcher handles to the pulley ropes. With deft efficiency and ease, the litter with patient on board was "elevatored" up the shaft by winching the lines from below. Barnes, his bodyguard, and the other litter bearer climbed the ladders and disconnected the stretcher at the top from its fixed position to which it had been raised.

Five-foot-high mine shafts shot off in two opposing directions on the lift's upper level. The carriers took the one on the right. Within less than ten yards the tunnel transformed into a shovel excavated entryway to a large elongated hut, sunken like a cellar and roofed at ground level with bamboo and thatching. Empty cots and sleeping mats lined the planked floor. Thick canopy camouflaged the whole installation, making it totally invisible to air reconnaissance.

Waiting inside the structure were Inger and Greta who immediately took charge of the post-op patient—under the ever-watchful eye of his mother. Once the child was unstrapped from the litter, he was placed in a semi-seated position, which he tolerated. He was still quite warm in spite of the climate of the cave.

The task of transporting the patient completed, Barnes was ushered back into the tunnel by armed escort and returned to the surgery section of the cave. As if to reward him, Barnes was permitted to remain with Claire while Ming pondered his decision about her future disposition.

The earthen floor was cool as was the stone wall against which Barnes crouched and compressed the curvature of his back for comfort. The moisture made each surface feel colder, especially the mud which oozed between his toes. Claire lay on the cot beside him in the quiet cocoon of a coma. Every now and then Barnes would lean forward and check her pulse. After each examination his fingers would gently massage her forearm and arm, stroking toward her shoulder. His touch was light as he brushed the nape of her neck with the back of his hand. He used every form of tactile stimulation—to communicate that someone was there—that she was not alone. Claire was unresponsive. Her whole body lay motionless, even though her movements would have been greatly restricted by the restraints applied for her safety.

With regard to testing her state of consciousness, Barnes was hesitant to apply more painful stimuli like deep muscle pinching. She seemed so restful. The diffracted lighting from the outer room accentuated her natural beauty, in spite of the gaunt features of her profile. To Barnes, she was the epitome of angelic.

At the conclusion of one caressing pass, Barnes teased and twisted the tip of one of the few remaining tresses of hair which had escaped the pre-op prepper's blade—one curling tuft exposed from beneath the turban-like bandage which haloed her head. Claire moved. She attempted to flex her left arm. She bent her hand at the wrist against the strap as if to acknowledge the contact and to brush the lock back into place. Barnes stroked her cheek; Claire vocalized a sigh. He called her by name; she opened her eyes and looked searchingly into his. He grasped her hand; she squeezed it lightly then released her grip, her wrist and hand dropping to the cot. Her condition of semi-consciousness was short-lived as she resumed a stuporous state.

Barnes managed a smile which no one could see and his eyes moistened in spite of being robbed of tears by dehydration. "Thank you, Lord!" The joy of the moment was softening a chronically calloused heart.

Throughout the night, Barnes talked tenderly and whispered

softly into Claire's ear. He recited the twenty-third Psalm emphasizing and personalizing the words.

"The Lord is *your* shepherd, Claire. Yea though *you* walk *through,* not stay in, the valley of the shadow of death, goodness and mercy shall follow *you, Claire. You* shall dwell in the house of the Lord forever. *You, Claire!"*

He repeated the Lord's Prayer to her as she slept. He reminded her that God loved her, and that Adam loved her more.

Barnes surprised himself with these last audacious words of hyperbola. Barnes knew God loved Claire more than he, but for some reason he had not felt like *God was there*—though spiritually he knew the promise that *He* was "with (us) always." Barnes rationalized that Claire just needed to hear these words from someone who was near—someone gently touching her skin with his.

This appointed time experience of joy, which Barnes so desperately was seeking to have fulfilled in his life, was interrupted abruptly by a flashlight shining in his eyes.

"Doctor Barnes. Doctor Barnes."

It was Greta. The colonel's son was not doing well. After one attempt at walking, the boy became faint and collapsed. His body temperature was spiking, and his bandages were soaked with blood. The nurse had been sent to fetch the American.

Once more crouching, crawling, and bounding bent over almost on all fours, they made their way through the tunnels to the ladders—bodyguard closely behind as if in tow. Navigating the labyrinthine passages was like traversing the darkened path that exists between the state of joy and the state of apprehension—the first, independent of circumstances; the second, totally associated with what has happened or will happen in the future.

Exiting from the underground tunnel, Barnes continued a

review of various medical scenarios: whether operating in a hurry had he missed a punctate rupture in a necrotic appendix, an intra-abdominal abscess hidden somewhere in the pelvis, or had he seeded the gut with infection from the inflamed appendage? Fevers were common but this seemed awfully high for a post-op one—106 degrees. A fulminant infection was the bane of every post-op recovery and Barnes believed today the curse had caught him.

The pristine, white, germ-free environment of hospital settings stateside presented a challenge to replicate in Vietnam, especially beyond the fixed urban centers. Failure to observe the principle of aseptic surgical technique was common to the practice of medicine in the field, though mostly an unintentional act. Wounds and incisions were inadvertently contaminated from the moment of their existence. Bacteria-laden flies, dust, and dirt would infiltrate an exposed surgical site unhindered. Lacerations were culture media for microorganisms. And yet penicillin had maintained super warrior status since the day when Sir Alexander Fleming first discovered the healing properties of that fungus. Vietnam's "bugs" of the modern era had never encountered such a ferocious infection fighter, even though some penicillin-resistant strains of bacteria had developed, most notably in the category of venereal disease. Yet, with the indigenous population, penicillin remained a more than conquering hero against infection.

Barnes believed that large doses of penicillin could turn the tide in his patient's favor without more surgery. He hoped in hope itself that Inger and Greta may have hoarded away the drug for personal emergencies, their channels and timetables of resupply being inconsistent in the war. Not a single vial or pill dose of any antibiotic was available. However, prisoner Barnes had a plan B. He did know where some penicillin could be found—procurable from a place only hours away.

As a medical officer, Barnes was permitted to carry out MED-CAP sessions while visiting the artillery batteries on Nui Ba Dinh. In his *official* army capacity he was part of the medical assistance program. *Unofficially,* these were personal visits to work with an old friend, one closer than even Barnes would acknowledge at the time. Now, he would. His sadness was that Claire might never know how much he really cared.

In the mission dispensary, Barnes recalled seeing a few vials of penicillin G powder that could be reconstituted for intramuscular injection or as an intravenous infusion. One IM injection could work wonders in giving the young patient's immune system a boost for battling the infection.

His plan was to negotiate the release of the hostage, Claire, in exchange for retrieving the penicillin for Colonel Ming's son. The shot could save the boy's life if he could receive it before sunrise. His condition was deteriorating rapidly, based on what Greta had told Barnes.

Major Thieu represented the key to this plan in communicating urgency to the father. Thieu could get Claire back to the hilltop mission and convince the missionaries at the orphanage of his need of penicillin. The staff there would honor the request because of Claire and because of the Montagnard link that Thieu had with the people of the mountain. The major was probably the only one who had the credibility for the checkpoints and with the locals to pull off the various intricacies of this nighttime exchange plan. Barnes was counting on the missionaries to get a MEDEVAC dust-off for the first thing in the morning. Claire would get the emergency treatment she needed and would be on a "freedom bird" to the Philippines for recovery, and then home for rehabilitation.

Major Thieu made the proposal to Colonel Ming, still awake and in the TOC busily coordinating battle plans for the next day. Thorough preparation required strategies for attack, for hunkering down in the underground complex, for counter attack and if need be, for retreat and withdrawal to the North. The colonel needed no prolonged distractions, a point in favor of the negotiator, Thieu. Considering his own healing experience with penicillin on his past facial wound, the Viet Cong commander was most persuasive in the short time the NVA colonel allowed him to speak.

"See to it!"

The accepted plan was operational. Ming's attention returned to his staff and the array of maps on the table.

Claire made the circuitous journey through the tunnels, up the vent shaft by winch, through the recovery area in the nurses' cellar ward. The bearers stopped for Barnes to make one last check of her condition. Medically, Barnes had no certitude that she could survive the ruggedness of the trip they were about to undertake, but it was her only chance to get the medical care she needed. Spiritually, he confirmed that this "concession" to let her go into greater hands than his, was undeniably the right choice.

Arrangements had been made for Claire's litter to be loaded onto a water buffalo cart, a safer form of transportation for this night excursion across enemy lines. Inger volunteered to accompany Claire in the cart. Claire's vital signs were encouraging to Barnes as she progressed up the arousal scale of her semi-comatose state.

Barnes, kneeling at her side, whispered into the ear of his unconscious friend, "Remember, the Lord is *your shepherd.* He is leading you to still waters and green pastures. Don't be afraid."

He kissed her forehead in the same manner as he had done that night in San Francisco, but added the words he had refrained from saying that night.

"Claire, I love you."

Barnes assisted as the stretcher was hoisted up and secured in the cart. After the mini-caravan of Thieu, Inger, the two carriers, and Claire vanished into the glade of bamboo trees which bordered the village, the generator could be heard in the distance to sputter then trigger to life.

Using the second flashlight now restored with new batteries, Barnes made one more examination of the post-op child with the begrudging consent of the mama-san, who sat in the traditional squat on the dirt floor. She made no sound and had no physical contact with her son. It was as if she were observing a wake vigil. Yet she paid steely eyed attention in the shadows to every move the doctor or Nurse Greta made regarding her child.

A waning crescent moon greeted Barnes as he stepped from beneath the thatch of the hospital hut. The American captive was being returned to his prison cage. Looking up at the celestial lights, he was able faintly to detect on a distant ridge the cart which was carrying Claire back to Nui Ba Dinh. Within seconds, the two-wheeler wagon disappeared around a bend in the path— first the plodding draft animal and the herdsman with his goad, next the big wheels, and finally the tilted flatbed. As he watched, he wondered whether he would ever see Claire again. A forceful nudge in the back intruded on his pensive pause; and when

Barnes resumed his peering into the dark, the cart was out of view. And Claire was gone.

At the cage a half-full bucket of water and a single rice bowl awaited him. An extra large portion mounded up out of the bowl. Barnes was rewarded with the privilege of sitting outside the box to eat. Therefore, he chose to dine as if this were his last meal of freedom. He took his time to savor every grain he could capture by feel with his fingers.

When he finished the contents and washed them down with a final gulp from the bamboo dipper, Barnes was directed to fold himself back inside his cell. The guard secured it shut. For Barnes, the exhaustion of the day had overtaken him in the night. His body ached from the crooked posturing he had to endure while performing surgery in a cubbyhole, and his bare feet burned from the shuffling and shuttling in the tunnels. The fetal position in the confines of the cage felt good. Sleep came instantaneously the moment his balled up body relaxed. Barnes was utterly unaware that today he should have been home in the U.S.A.

CHAPTER 34

DEROS FOR HEROES
GOING HOME

The morning mist was being dissolved by first light breaking through the gaps in the jungle foliage. A foraging water buffalo persistently bumped against Barnes' prison cage trying to dislodge a lone tuft of elephant grass sprouting out from beneath the bamboo floor. The same animal, which had toiled through the night towing the ambulance wagon, now being unhitched was ready to eat. A hemp rope tied around one of the bison beast's hind legs and anchored to a central peg limited its grazing access up to the hut piling beside the cage.

The bumping jolts and the annoying noise of chomping jaws were awakening Barnes from the midst of a dream, or more accurately, a nightmare. The setting in his sleep was an earthquake and he was attempting to crawl out of a crevasse as its walls were collapsing. (Since childhood, being swallowed up and buried alive had been Barnes' ultimate phobia.) In this vision, the sliding soil entombed his legs up to his knees with suction like in quicksand; he could not move no matter how much he struggled. Visibility overhead was veiled by a haze of dust particles. Clods of clay were caroming off his cheeks and pebbles were painfully pelting his lips. Yet, the dirt coming in contact with his face was real. The water buffalo actually was churning up rocks and lumps of soil as it pawed at the entrapped stalks of straw.

Arousal from a nightmarish reverie to a nightmarish reality is a shock to anyone's senses. But being tired and worn, Barnes had no energy for the emotions of shock. He knew Vietnam was not a game. It was a war. And *war* had become *hell* for him.

Rubbing his eyes, Barnes noted that the cage flap was hooked open and his breakfast bowl of rice—half full garnished with a layer of early arriving flies—was both beckoning and repulsing him at the same time. Just steps away, his overseer was squatted next to that two-wheeled cart tilted against a wooden watering trough. The Viet Cong soldier appeared prepared for battle: shirtless and shoeless, shorts belted with a cord, a leather sapper's pouch, and a full ammo bandolier slung over his shoulder across his chest. His AK-47 rifle was leaning against the cart. He was one of Major Thieu's men; and though he was charged to guard the prisoner, he may have been assigned by Thieu to be Barnes' bodyguard protector. Barnes was not sure which.

As the American captive finished his insect-seasoned ration of rice, the Viet Cong soldier stood up with his rifle in hand. His cadre chief had just exited from a nearby bunker and was approaching the two men.

Thieu updated Barnes that Nurse Claire endured the trip and was being cared for by the Montagnard missionaries. In spite of the fighting in the valley they had remained on the mountain to look after the children. He could not confirm if the orphanage director had called for a MEDEVAC airlift, but Thieu did corroborate that the American artillery battery was back launching fire missions off of Nui Ba Dinh. In addition, he told Barnes that before leaving Nurse Claire at the orphanage and setting out on the return trip to Cambodia early that morning, Nurse Inger had given her a shot of penicillin. Barnes expressed his thanks to the major whose report had engendered a sense of hopefulness for Claire while yielding a heartening of the spirit for Adam.

Later, as Barnes was escorted through the village to check on the colonel's son, he perceived a strange quiescence, like the calm which permeates the atmosphere before a storm. The whole hamlet displayed a state of dormancy, as if everyone had made a conscious decision to sleep in, or hide out, that morning.

The first set of villager's eyes the army physician encountered at the recovery hooch belonged to the patient's mother. She was standing and waiting at the doorway. Her body language betrayed little, but her eyes projected a gaze of gratitude. She intentionally brushed his hand as he entered and followed him inside where Nurse Greta was carefully spooning a watery rice soup into the mouth of the young lad. He was weak but amazingly alert. His condition, Greta confirmed, had begun to improve within an hour of his first injection of penicillin. Undefeated and still champion.

Echoic whomps in the distance shattered the tranquil stillness. The sound of exploding artillery rounds contacting the ground initiated the alarm. Pajama-clad NVA regulars appeared out of nowhere and scurried like rats into the spiderweb network of tunnels. The underground bomb shelters were filling up fast. The rumor that the American forces had withdrawn from the border during the night was just that—a rumor.

An unchallenged confidence existed among the enemy on the premise preached that the North Vietnamese could outlast the U.S and ARVN assaults on the Fishhook border provinces. The NVA and the Viet Cong were being energized by their belief that this would be the last aerial bombardment before monsoon season and that soon it would be their turn to retaliate en masse. They would strike across the Cambodian border, deep into the heart of South Vietnam, right up to the very outskirts of the capital, Saigon.

Though Barnes' security clearance authorized him to view classified documents at a high level, as a field officer his access was for all practical purposes limited in the top-secret category of offensive strategies that might be coming down the pike. The Americans had studied carefully the patterns of attack of its enemy and now were about to apply a military stratagem learned from their opponent. It would be on a much larger scale than when implemented by the Communist insurgents. The enemy militants would be engaged where they lived. "Search and destroy" had been the mission policy. Now the <u>search</u> was over. It was time to <u>destroy</u>. No longer die for a tie. No longer fighting with one hand behind the back. No longer playing not to lose. ***Vietnam was not a game! It was a war!***

Barnes was aware of the tactical scheme of diversion used by the enemy in its simplest form. Magicians used misdirection as a diversionary technique to pull off their sleight-of-hand illusions. Wartime armies used diversionary movements to disarm, distract, and drive the herd into a specific kill zone. Military diversions in battle were designed as tricks to allay fears and to divert attention from the actual point of attack until it was time for the death trap to be sprung on the unsuspecting.

American forces had been experimenting with multiple ways to deal with the "Tunnel Alley" link at the end of the Ho Chi Minh Trail for some time. A more extensive approach than sending brave tunnel rats with C-4 satchel charges was being sought. The aerial assault method was unproven, especially against the deeper tunnels. (Field intelligence confirmed that these complexes underneath the ground, if destroyed, would eventually and inevitably be rebuilt—it was astounding what an army of worker ants, determined to dig, could accomplish in such a short time.)

Whenever a territory was found to be infested with underground infiltration routes, a joint operation was coordinated between the army artillery and the air force. The first stage was to wage a cannonade campaign with hefty howitzers shelling the area. The intent of such a barrage was to force the Cong and NVA soldiers beneath ground and into their system of tunnels. Barnes was familiar with this fire mission-phase from his days with the 1st/30th Battalion.

The second step incorporated an arc-light saturation bombing by the air force. On several occasions from their perch upon Nui Ba Dinh, Dr. Barnes and Nurse Marshall had observed in action the B-52 bombers "laying carpet" on the valley floor below and had witnessed the spectacular air shows in the sky by the F-4 Phantom jets. Barnes had often wondered what it was like for the enemy to undergo such a "shock-and-awe" bombardment. Now he knew. Even the term, "terrifying," could not descriptively do justice to what actually happens.

In the underworld rather than on the mountaintop, Barnes marveled at and placed reliance on the ingenuity of the tunnel-making moles to keep themselves safe, barring a direct hit. Yet unlike before, today something seemed different. The second chorus of seismic concussions seemed spaced out in time and fewer in number. To create the variations in tone which Barnes was distinguishing, the pattern would have to be one of deliberate delays in detonation rather than the rapid-fire, staccato sound of a carpet bombing pass. The bomb bursts also were bunched—three distinct clusters, only three. Barnes' apprehension antennae went up, "What Is Coming? What if the rumors were true? Had the Americans pulled back to their bases in Vietnam?" Barnes dreaded the answer but reasoned, "If so, then why only an arc-light of three clusters? What is coming?"

The initial artillery strike had been close enough to the village to disrupt the supply of electricity again. Beneath the domed canopy the droning of the generator could be heard modulating to a lower pitch—still audible but sputtering.

The Montagnard, Major Thieu, came running through the ward pointing at Barnes. "If want live, come now!" Thieu had a flashlight. The hooch cleared as everyone dashed into the trenched access to the tunnels. With assistance, so did the NVA colonel's son. At the silo, some went down the ladders while others circled around the hole and continued on the same level. Barnes followed the groups with Thieu down the ladders.

At the bottom in the roundhouse room, the center of the spiderweb network of passages, Thieu headed deeper into the belly of the earth down a tunnel branch that led in the opposite direction from the surgical suite. Barnes hesitated. Then he ducked into a nearby cul-de-sac cache and hid behind a stack of ammunition boxes. He could feel the ballistic pounding of his heart against his chest wall. He unrealistically feared that the cardiac drumbeat would betray his position in the dark.

The absence of light beams verified that no one was coming back to check on him. Huddled behind the supply crates, Barnes began to formulate a plan to execute an escape. Separating from Thieu and the light was a risk he would take to be free. Predominant in his mind was the terror-laden thought, "I don't want to be buried alive!"

If he could make it back to the nurses' hooch and survive all the incoming chaos, Barnes believed he could eventually venture east, hiding out during the day and traveling at night. Within a day he would be able to see Nui Ba Dinh towering up off the plain as the lone topographic landmark. That sighting would be all he would need. Based on Major Thieu's report, his old unit was still entrenched at its mountaintop firebase.

Scampering back up the ladder in the dark, he heard and encountered no one coming down. At the top, he started crawling on all fours toward the recovery ward twenty yards away, when the ceiling shelf began to collapse at the entryway to the hooch. The tiny sprays of light filtering through the outer thatchings and through the inner bunker bags were rapidly shut out by the subsequent cave-in. The crushing sound suggested that the remainder of the upper tunnel was on the verge of falling in on him too.

Barnes reversed on his belly and slid his probing arms back toward the mine silo as a blind man might move his cane from side to side to test for obstacles in his way. Barnes could not afford to fall head first down the shaft. His fingers finally reached the pit rim as support timbers behind him could be heard to topple over like an approaching row of dominoes. He groped over the edge and grasped the first rung on the nearest ladder. Then he swiveled his legs and lower body 180 degrees into the hole as rock and earth came crushing down on the spot where his body had lain just a second before. Dirt was falling like a heavy hailstorm down into the mineshaft making a plunking sound as pieces struck the sides, the ladders, and the bedrock below. Barnes was afraid the ceiling support would not hold; and if it disintegrated, the falling chunks of debris could knock him off the ladder before he could reach the bottom.

Since the ventilation flow had been greatly altered by the

cave-ins and the slime mold coating of the walls was contaminating the residual air, a more intense, musty odor permeated the tunnels. The stagnant smell was nauseating. Barnes' breathing was becoming more stifled and labored with the lack of fresh air. Deep inhalations were avoided.

In the pit, every move which Barnes made was preceded by a probing foot or feeling fingers. The moisture and the resultant muddied rungs were making the descent slippery and treacherous. Failing to secure four points of contact on the ladder, his hand grip slipped. His inertial impetus tilted his trunk away from the wall, and in order not to land awkwardly on his back, he jumped to maintain verticality. He estimated the bottom was near. It was nearer than he thought. He crumpled hard to the ground severely twisting his left ankle.

On the floor now, to escape the dropping debris, Barnes pulled himself away from the center of the shaft and scooted beneath one of the wooden benches positioned against the wall. Apparently that third cluster strike had set off chain reaction quakes throughout the region resulting in these underground compressions and collapses.

Even though Barnes was familiar with this core chamber, the darkness and the fall had disoriented and dazed him. But then he heard it, a faint vibration, a hum so rhythmic that it had to be man-made and mechanical. Only the generator could be transmitting that sound along the layers of stone. The cadent noise was evident in the tunnel passageway to his left. His journey out would start there. The generator represented the destination point for fresh air and freedom.

Far up the tunnel he trudged, crawling again on knees and hands. Then he discovered a blessing—flickering light ahead.

The illumination was activating the doctor's night vision. It was beyond adequate. When Barnes reached the first candle, he could see that a few more emergency ones had been lit in the wall shelves along the passageway, though sparsely placed. He took the first one with him, cupping his hand in front to protect the flame from extinguishing. With a light to guide him, Barnes picked up the pace.

Touching the tunnel wall with the back of his leading shoulder, Barnes shuffled his way toward where he remembered the surgery lair to be located. Because of his ankle injury, he employed a short, sidestepping stride like a crab—a slow but stable gait. He confronted no enemy personnel, so he assumed that all of them had descended to the security of a deeper level of which he was unaware.

The emitted sound from the generator was getting louder and Barnes was becoming more confident that he knew where he was. The widening corridor along which he limped opened up into a candlelit room. He was back at the "surgery."

After a brief scavenging for matches and the nurses' flashlight, neither of which could be found, Barnes crawled into the recovery alcove to hide and rest. At one point a rat, separated from its pack, shot into the same dead-end vault. As the doctor attempted to catch his breath, the rodent scampered up his leg and perched on his bent knee. Startled by the sensation, Adam in a reflex snapped his leg down. The rat spun in reverse and scurried away resuming its frenetic search for a way out of the rapidly deteriorating environ.

Unfortunately, adrenaline would not allow the doctor to rest. A foreboding anxiety stimulated every fiber of his being. He was so near the outside and freedom that the constant chugging of the generator beckoned him like a voice to come on up. The summoning sound was so enticing that he acquiesced. Now or never, he agreed, was the time to move.

Finding some strips of bandage material, and an NVA flag, he chose to wrap his bare feet with the dressing gauze in preparation for the jungle journey on hardened paths and rough-cut roads to Nui Ba Dinh. He left the flag behind respecting the symbol of his rival.

With his sprained ankle puffing up, he recalculated it might take him two days instead of one to reach the mountain. Nonetheless, he was confident he could make it even if he had to crawl on his hands and knees all the way.

Barnes negotiated around overturned tables, saw horses, and stretchers, slowly advancing to the foot of the hatch ladder mounted on the wall. The trap door egress at the top would flop back for access to the passageway through which he had first entered this frightful underworld. His captivity seemed an eternity in time, but actually he had been a prisoner for less than three days.

Faintly streaming through the bamboo slats at the top of the ladder came lines of light. From below, Barnes had not noticed them as they blended in with the flickering rays of the candlewick; but now, with his elevated perspective, they were quite defined by intensity as they fell across his chest and refracted across the shadowy floor.

The freed captive considered retreating down the ladder since in his mind the tunnel above should have been in total darkness. That is how he remembered the conditions on his initial, forced crawl. However, the glimmer radiating from around the edges caused him, out of curiosity, to raise the hatch. In the distance he saw one single sliver of light—natural light, not from an artificial source like a bulb or a flashlight.

Squeezing through the narrow aperture, Barnes contorted his long frame into the contour of the clay culvert above. Nothing seemed familiar except for the cramped feeling of being crammed into a corridor designed to accommodate individual bodies much smaller than his own.

The one noted improvement was the presence of light—light filtering through the intermittent curtain of falling dust particles. Structural changes in the passageway now included mounded piles of loose dirt. These uneven heaps had been deposited all along this fifty-foot section of tunnel, still somewhat intact after the first wave of detonations. How long it would remain sound and solid was a valid question for Barnes as he began his venture through the earthen pipeline.

Complicating this concern, the frightful image of being buried alive was pressing in on Barnes' inner psyche from all directions. Mentally, with every ounce of concentration, he was trying to push his childhood phobia out to a more comfortable, less threatening, position on the periphery of his thoughts. However, the quaking, crumbling tube which compressed him physically, was a tactile reminder reinforcing the reality that it could happen—a life-crushing collapse. Smothering. Suffocating. And *soon*.

Adam inched along dragging his injured leg limply behind him. With one hand he covered his mouth using his T-shirt as a filter. With the other, he sifted through the softened soil for something more firm with which to propel himself. During his next outstretched stroke he came in contact with *something* in the sand—something rounded. Then that something moved. Whatever it was, it had two tails. Since the contact was only fleeting, a definitive determination could not be made as to what it was. All Barnes could discern was that his fingers had briefly engaged and entwined two tail-like cords as his hand raked over the mass in the mound of dirt.

Simultaneously, a hiss was heard and a menacing flash of bared fangs was seen. Rising up in the middle of the burrow as an umbral stalk silhouetted against the daylight haloing the end of the tunnel was a snake—hooded and huge from the perspective of up close and personal. The human froze. The reptile froze. The standoff seemed to last for an eternity. When the snake's erect shadow slowly dissolved into the dirt, Barnes detected the subtle, serpentine turning away. With its progress having been interrupted, it was now slowly slithering forward again with knotted cord in tow.

At that moment, the only thing between Barnes and escape from the underground was that last sentinel. A perilous quake behind. A poisonous snake ahead. The clock was ticking down. Adam reasoned he could not turn back; neither could he stay put and wait! Without thinking further, he reached after the elongated viper. Grabbing the extended tail, he snatched the snake back behind him in one whip-like motion. After the quick release of the tail, Barnes rolled over on his back and began heaving handfuls of dirt at the target below his bandaged feet. He hoped to discourage his reptilian rival, at the least, from following for the time being. It was the obstacle course from basic training all over again, and Barnes still was determined to be the first one out of the trench.

Just ahead, some toppling of the support beams had created a tortuous trough complicated by sections where the ceiling had collapsed. Barnes wormed his way along, sliding over and around mounds of dirt, digging out and under slanted timbers and wedged boulders. He concluded that the higher tunnel had caved down on the lower level of the excavated trench. Instead of the tightly tapered opening at the end of the tunnel, a slash in the earth had peeled apart, creating a narrow and extended crevice. To the east the sky was visible, jungle cover having been ripped asunder by the force of the shell bursts in the tree line.

Like a bolt out of the powdery blue, sonic footprints stepped onto the stage of this surrealistic scene to interrupt a comparative lull in the aerial spectacle. Barnes was still below stage in an orchestra pit/ditch, immersed deep in mounting heaps of clay, when he heard the "walk." The earth trembled. Barnes imagined a gigantic King Kong striding across the jungle plantations.

The booming "footsteps" were distant, but still so much more resounding than any round of a mortar or a rocket. In fact, Barnes had never been exposed to sound waves with such a high decibel magnitude. He instinctively cupped his ears to protect his hearing but it was too late. The concussion, painfully sharp, ruptured both eardrums. From the instant of the first thunderous clap to the second, Barnes estimated it to be about five seconds; but all passage of time seemed to have lapsed into slow motion. Yet for Adam he felt freeze-framed in space.

The ground-level surface stood ten feet above the trench in which Barnes was crawling. Beyond that, the openness of space. As he looked skyward, a sparkling reflection of the sun's rays glinted down from the stratosphere. The silver speck was undoubtedly a plane streaking stealthily across the heavens—one solitary aircraft—probably a B-52 he thought.

All at once this point of light was diffused into an explosive flash brighter than the sun. The whole sky was lit up by its blinding brilliance. Absolutely nothing was visible except the light. Everything coalesced with it.

As the physical surroundings reemerged visually into focused recognition, an unnatural roar of thunder came rumbling from the west as if a sonic reservoir had burst open and every pent up amplification had been released. White light and white noise had stimulated Barnes' senses of sight and sound to the maximum— and beyond!

———————

Five minutes earlier and ten miles farther south in Vietnam, a single 707 troop transport had lifted off from Ton San Nhut Air Base. The first rain of the monsoon season was gently splashing down on the cockpit window as the pilots listened to the control tower. Air traffic personnel were reiterating emphatically their flight instructions to head due south, toward the peninsular tip of the country before turning east over the Mekong Delta and out across the South China Sea. Air space over Cambodia and III Corps South Vietnam had been designated a *code red no-fly zone.*

Just before the aircraft reached cruising altitude, its wings began to vibrate as sequential sonic shock waves buffeted the jet plane. An onboard cheer of joy was transformed into a groan and temporarily stifled with the sudden tossing and dipping sensations in the fuselage cabin.

Located in the forward section of the plane, a civilian passenger sat grimacing as she reclined in a seat which had been modified for transporting seriously injured soldiers. The commotion had startled her to consciousness. Noticing the patient's wincing movements, a flight attendant rushed up the aisle to her side.

"Are you all right?" she inquired.

"What was that noise?" the patient uttered with a tremulous voice.

"Just shouting from some jubilant soldiers who are headed home after a year in the war. It happens every time we leave Vietnam airspace," the flight nurse replied, trying not to show any undue concern over the excessive turbulence.

As the aircraft leveled off, it banked left revealing one final glimpse of the country landscape now far below. Claire Marshall craned her bandaged head toward the plane's porthole. Bulging up out of the distant horizon, an iridescent arch enclosed three enormous plumes of cumulous symmetry. Gradually, the mushroom-shaped clouds spread out concentrically from separate axial points of detonation. Ballooning miles into the atmosphere, the three fireball orbs eventually began to merge at their bulbous extremes—an imposing vista so spectacular as to be almost unbelievable.

Noting the expression on Claire's face, the flight nurse leaned down to observe what Claire was viewing. Overwhelmed with awe, the nurse murmured, *"Oh…my…God!"*

As she did, the plane began to vibrate again, more violently propelled by the additional impetus of shock waves.

Back in Cambodia, from his perilous crumbling pit, U.S. Army Captain Adam Barnes exclaimed, *"They did it! I can't believe they actually did it!"*

The doctor at DEROS quit struggling with the dirt and rolled over on his back, eyes searching beyond the new cosmic canopy.

Two shouts, the same single word in the affirmative repeated, "Yes!" (It's over!) "Yes!" (I'm going home!)

The firestorm, associated with these thermodynamic blasts created an inundating avalanche of surface debris and glowing gusts of fallout dust. Swirling clouds increasingly impeded any view of the sky—translucent lightness transitioned into obstructive opaqueness—and finally the black starkness of darkness.

"Lord, be merciful to me, sinner that I am. Thanks, I bring to you, in advance. Into your hands, I concede my…"

In the midst of this final prayer, the earth beneath him fell away. The ground collapsed into an open pit and Adam Barnes was swallowed up in victory!

It was DEROS day!

"Then shall the dust return to the earth as it was; and the spirit shall return unto God who gave it." (Eccles.12:7)

It was DEROS day!

And yet, beneath, in an instant, a twinkling in the eye of night. *Deep…down…distant…*drawing expansively across the darkness like the dawning bathe of the sun, entered the Light of Life.

Was it DEROS day?

EPILOGUE

While leisurely strolling the sidewalks and footpaths of the Mall of Memorials in the nation's capital of Washington, D.C., up ahead, artistically tasteful but understated, a bulwark of polished black granite meets the eye. Merging almost imperceptibly with its background, the tall stone partitions loom up, embedded against an earthen embankment. Well groomed but concealed, the Vietnam Veterans Memorial lines the landscape, angling like a formidable wall of containment.

Etched as with silver into this tablet of rock are the names of 58,000 servicemen who experienced DEROS far before their life-expected times. Prematurely in war overseas, they died in the support of their comrades and in the service of their country during the span of years between 1956 and 1975—the highest rate of casualties being from the State of West Virginia.

To the west of the wall on a slight rise amidst a sparse grove of sheltering trees, three infantry soldiers stand. Posed in dark bronze, they have been sculpted as pausing for one last revering gaze at the Memorial headstone. DEROS day for them would seem to lie beyond, just over the horizon, at some future point in the hereafter.

Both the wall and the warriors who symbolically "walk point" represent the **undefeated** who once fought for freedom in Vietnam. Within the *"league"* of nations—contrary to popular public opinion—members of this team in head-to-head, hand-to-hand competition never suffered defeat. Their flag still stands un-captured. A star-spangled banner still waves in the land of the free and the home of the brave.

May American citizens **always remember** with grateful hearts our Vietnam Veterans and their victory as champions of freedom in that season of battles. And **never forget** the misinformed and misguided who forfeited what they considered to be a **Game** and not a **War**, being naïve to the collateral consequences for countries controlled by totalitarian regimes. May the forfeiters of freedom be forgiven for subsequently, and in some rare cases unsympathetically, letting so many of those **WITHOUT A DEROS** suffer and die in vain—in Vietnam, in Cambodia, in Laos, and throughout Southeast Asia. From the womb and through a war, they—as do we all—had their one chance in a lifetime for a lifetime. However, by the millions, each solitary life, unique and unrivaled, was taken from them and lost forever. Someday, would that the terrorized innocents surviving in these countries could escape the tyranny of untruth and taste true freedom and the personal peace that surpasses all understanding.

Lord of All,

Please help the helpless and the hopeless
so tragically still under the oppression of authoritarian
rulers, religions, and regimes around the world...

and concerning those of us who know freedom
in America, for the continuance of our
constitutional liberties and inalienable rights,
a prayerful offering of

Thanks I Bring In Advance!